CHRIS

AN AMERICAN ANNUAL OF CHR

EDITED BY RANDOLPH E. HAUGAN · VOLUME NUMBER TEN

TMAS

ISTMAS LITERATURE AND ART

AUGSBURG PUBLISHING HOUSE · PUBLISHERS · MINNEAPOLIS

VOLUME TEN · FIRST EDITION
NINETEEN HUNDRED AND FORTY

Table of Contents

Three Kings

United they kneel at the manger bed
After their long trek over the sand:
Three valiant kings who were strangely led
By a silver light to a far-off land.

Weighted with gifts of jewels and gold,
The shine of the star still in their eyes,
Caspar, Melchior, Balthazar hold
In their hearts the wisdom of all the wise.

Humbly before the Christ they wait,
Acknowledging Him, His glory, His power,
There at His side they subjugate
Their will to His this radiant hour.

Their burdens lift from their hearts, they rise,
Men with a vision... they turn, they go
Back to their own far lands, these wise
Earnest kings of the long ago.

Oh, that earth's rulers today would take
The starlit road to the Christ, and there,
Seeking a cure for the world's heart-break,
Find it in humble, united prayer!

Grace Noll Crowell

The Christmas Gospel · According to St. Luke and St. Matthew

AND it came to pass in those days, that there went out a decree from Cæsar Augustus, that all the world should be taxed. (And this taxing was first made when Cyrenius was governor of Syria.) And all went to be taxed, every one into his own city. And Joseph also went up from Galilee, out of the city of Nazareth, into Judæa, unto the city of David, which is called Bethlehem; (because he was of the house and lineage of David:) to be taxed with Mary his espoused wife, being great with child. And so it was, that, while they were there, the days were accomplished that she should be delivered. And she brought forth her firstborn Son, and wrapped Him in swaddling clothes, and laid Him in a manger; because there was no room for them in the inn. ¶And there were in the same country shepherds abiding in the field, keeping watch over their flock by night. And, lo, the angel of the Lord came upon them, and the glory of the Lord shone round about them: and they were sore afraid. And the angel said unto them, Fear not: for, behold, I bring you good tidings of great joy, which shall be to all people. ¶For unto you is born this day in the city of David a Saviour, which is Christ the Lord. And this shall be a sign unto you; Ye shall find the Babe wrapped in swaddling clothes, lying in a manger. And suddenly there was with the angel a multitude of the heavenly host praising God, and saying, Glory to God in the highest, and on earth peace, good will toward men. ¶And it came to pass, as the angels were gone away from them into heaven, the shepherds said one to another, Let us now go even unto Bethlehem, and see this thing which is come to pass, which the Lord hath made known unto us. And they came with haste, and found Mary, and Joseph, and the Babe lying in a manger. And when they had seen it, they made known abroad the saying which was told them concerning this Child. And all they that heard it wondered at those things which were told them by the shepherds. But Mary kept all these things, and pondered them in her heart. And the shepherds returned, glorifying and praising God for all the things that they had heard and seen, as it was told unto them.

NOW when Jesus was born in Bethlehem of Judæa in the days of Herod the king, behold, there came wise men from the East to Jerusalem, saying, Where is He that is born King of the Jews? For we have seen His star in the East, and are come to worship Him. When Herod the king had heard these things, he was troubled, and all Jerusalem with him. And when he had gathered all the chief priests and scribes of the people together, he demanded of them where Christ should be born. And they said unto him, In Bethlehem of Judæa: for thus it is written by the prophet, And thou Bethlehem, in the land of Juda, art not the least among the princes of Juda: for out of thee shall come a Governor, that shall rule my people Israel. Then Herod, when he had privily called the wise men, enquired of them diligently what time the star appeared. And he sent them to Bethlehem, and said, Go and search diligently for the young Child; and when ye have found Him, bring me word again, that I may come and worship Him also. When they had heard the king, they departed and, lo, the star, which they saw in the East, went before them, till it came and stood over where the young Child was. When they saw the star, they rejoiced with exceeding great joy. And when they were come into the house, they saw the young Child with Mary His mother, and fell down, and worshipped Him: and when they had opened their treasures, they presented unto Him gifts; gold, and frankincense, and myrrh. And being warned of God in a dream that they should not return to Herod, they departed into their own country another way.

Opposite page
The Holy Family
by Carlo Maratta

The Song of the Angels
BY HENRY KENDALL BOOTH

ISRAFEL the singer sat in a corner of the temple portico in gloomy discontent. The sun was flooding the great temple of Herod with light, blazing from its golden pinnacles, blindingly reflected from the dazzling whiteness of marble courts and colonnades. All about was the happy stir and murmur of the eager crowds that surged through the vast enclosure. Brightness and beauty were everywhere. Yet was Israfel moody and distraught. For his young soul was in a ferment of doubt and questioning. Until yesterday the morning practice of chant and antiphon under the chief cantor, the marching with his fellow-singers of the temple chorus through the stately measures of the liturgy, the daily routine of simple life and earnest labor had left him well content. And was not his the high honor by virtue of his marvelously-clear boyish voice to lead as soloist the vast congregation as he chanted the solemn stanzas of the Psalms?

But today the zest and freshness of life were gone, and in their place were doubt and discontent. And the cause was so trivial. For yesterday as he sat in the court of the Gentiles he had overheard two cultured Greeks discussing the music of the temple service. They declared its great bursts of hallelujahs, where the full chorus was supplemented by drums and trumpets, to be but barbarous noise, its monotonous unison chants prolonged on a single note to be a travesty on the sacred art of music. They then talked long and passionately of the music of Greece, with its beautiful flowing melodies and wonderful harmonies, so different from the barren and uncouth songs of this temple; with its rich orchestral accompaniments in such contrast to the crude and noisy instruments of these ignorant Jews. And as Israfel listened he was dismayed to find his first hot resentment succeeded by doubt and wonder. Certain murmurs of his own heart, quickly stilled, certain stirrings of his own spirit, instantly silenced, came to mind. And as in a flash he knew that all these were the inarticulate protest of his inward self against the monotonous, artificial chants, and noisy, blatant choruses of the temple liturgy. His musician's soul was

reaching out after higher things, and this mood of doubt and disillusionment in which he sat today was the first beating of the wings of genius against the bars of convention and circumstance. And, as he mused, an over-mastering desire seized him to fly from this temple and its service, out into the great world in search of that beautiful Greek music that might satisfy the longings of his soul.

He was awakened from his meditations by a touch upon his arm. He looked up into the face of Joseph, the servant of Heman, the chief cantor. "The Master would have speech with thee!" Swiftly he turned and departed and Israfel roused himself and followed.

In the chorus-hall of the temple sat Heman, the chief cantor, the arbiter of the music of Israel, next in authority to the high priest. Before him stood Israfel. Heman smiled at the lad as he waited the pleasure of the master, for Israfel's beauty, his sweet voice, his eager, ardent nature, had greatly endeared him to the old man. "Israfel, my son," said the chief cantor, "I have noted with approval your zeal and faithfulness, and I have chosen you because of your earnest study of our service, as my special messenger. The leader of music in the synagogue at Antioch is in doubt as to the rendering of the Great Hallel. I am sending you to him with this letter of introduction. Answer his questions, explain what he wishes to know, and then return to me. You will leave tomorrow. Peace be with you."

One week later Israfel stood in the presence of Asaph, leader of music in the synagogue at Antioch. Three hours he remained in his room chanting certain passages, explaining the form of certain measures. At last Asaph said, "My son, you have delighted me beyond measure with your knowledge and zeal. You must be weary. You will doubtless wish to see the sights of Antioch. You are free now to go at your pleasure."

His mission ended, Israfel left the synagogue with heart beating high with mingled hope and fear. All the long journey from Jerusalem to Antioch his mind had been intent upon the one thought, that his one great opportunity to hear the Greek music was before him. For in the great city of Antioch, more Greek than Syrian, he could satisfy his passionate and eager curiosity. Swiftly he passed through the streets of Antioch until he stood before the temple of Apollo. Long he lingered there, torn between the fear of heathen rites bred in him by the strict canons of his religion and that strong and eager desire of his musician's soul to hear the music of Hellas. But curiosity was stronger than fear, and he passed the pillared portico and entered. The air was heavy with incense, and the beautiful interior dim in the half-light that filtered through the lofty windows. Before the altar the white-robed priests were standing. Suddenly a strain of music from a hidden orchestra was heard, and from either side of the temple a group of choristers marched toward the altar. And as they met they burst into song. Slow, majestic, ineffably sweet, with flowing melodies that awoke the thoughts of carolling birds and rippling streams, the young voices of the boys began the hymn to Phoebus and the dawn; then, group after group, the men took up the strain until the whole temple rang with the majestic harmony, rich, full, entrancing.

And through it all Israfel stood as in a dream. Such beauty of melody he had never conceived, and the splendid concord of harmonies left him stunned and speechless. Long after the worshippers had passed out of the temple he stood there in rapture, his whole soul vibrant with the music that had swept his heartstrings.

It was in the same mood that the next day he turned his face homeward, and the spell of the ethereal music had not left him as he mechanically reported his mission to the chief cantor, and was dismissed to his room with kindly words of commendation. Once there, he sat long in abstraction on his couch, hearing again in memory those strains of rapturous beauty. His whole soul was filled with the passion of the artist. Seizing his lyre he began to sing. The words were the old familiar Great Hallel,

> "O give thanks unto the Lord; for He is good;
> For His lovingkindness endureth forever,"

but what was this marvelous melody that swelled higher and higher as he sang? Intricate, sweet, thrilling with passion, it was far removed from the crude and monotonous chants of the temple service. Over and over again he sang it, forgetful of time or place, rapt in the ecstasy of musical creation, his genius aflame with its power. Clear, sweet, strong, his young voice filled the whole hall and corridor. One and then another of his fellow-singers passed by his door to listen. Amazed, stupefied, they stood agape while Israfel sang on and on. Horror-stricken at the blasphemy that could couple those thrice-hallowed words with such passionate and unhallowed music, heathenish and wicked, they stood spellbound. Attracted by the gathering crowd, the chief cantor hurried down the corridor and joined the group before the door. One instant he listened, then the door was suddenly swung back and the lyre was dashed from Israfel's hands upon the floor. "Israfel, son of Simeon, what does this mean?" cried the chief cantor towering above the trembling lad. As one rudely awakened from a dream, Israfel stared dully at him, and answered not. "Answer me, sir, at once! Where did you hear this unhallowed music that has profaned your lips? How

dare you to blaspheme the most high God by singing His praises to the melodies of the accursed heathen?"

Falteringly, brokenly, Israfel told his story. The stern face of the chief cantor did not soften. Tender in other things, he was inflexible in his loyalty to the old music of the fathers, and that his favorite singer had thus sinned must be met by instant and condign punishment.

And so that night before a hastily summoned meeting of the officials of the temple, Israfel stood on trial. The eyes and hearts of these stern men softened not as they looked upon his youth and beauty. Swiftly and surely the sentence was spoken, and, stripped of his choral robes, disgraced and excommunicated from the Jewish church, a white-faced, tearful, trembling lad went out the temple gates an exile from his race and people.

The night was cold and clear, the sky studded with stars as Israfel stumbled blindly on through the streets of Jerusalem and took the road to Bethlehem. His sin as yet scarce realized, his punishment so swift, the lad was stunned as he found himself thus suddenly thrust out of the happy family of the temple-chorus into a hard and bitter world. Choking with sobs, scarce knowing where he went, he wandered on and on. It was near midnight when he reached Bethlehem. The inn was full to overflowing, and Israfel cared not to meet its crowds and curiosity, but went on up the slopes to the hillside above Bethlehem. Drawn by the light of a fire as by a beacon, scarce conscious of where he went, he suddenly came upon a group of shepherds asleep by the fire. As he stepped into the firelight an iron hand fell upon his shoulder and a harsh voice said, "What do you want here?" Trembling the lad began his answer, but as the sentinel shepherd saw his youthful face and tear-filled eyes, his grip relaxed and in a strangely softened voice he said, "Nay, nay, my lad. Tell your story in the morning. You are weary and worn. Lie down here by the fire and take a rest." And as Israfel dropped asleep, his last memory was the strong but kindly face of the shepherd as he gazed into the fire.

He was roused from slumber by a shout, "Awake! Awake!" He sprang to his feet in fear and amazement. The shepherds were gazing before them in wonder and as Israfel looked the whole hilltop above them seemed a mass of lambent flame and out of the flame stepped a glorious figure winged and majestic, and the shepherds and Israfel, blinded by the glory, fell on their faces in terror.

And then a voice spoke out of the glory, "Fear not!" Sweet and strong came the words, "Fear not! behold there is born this day in the city of David, a Saviour, which is Christ the Lord."

The voice ceased for a moment and then spoke again, "And this shall be a sign unto you. Ye shall find the babe wrapped in swaddling clothes and lying in a manger." There was silence for a time; at first faintly, and then clearly, came the rustle of wings until the whole air about them was full of whir and movement. Suddenly upon the still night rose the sound of the angelic choir,

> "Glory to God in the highest
> And on earth peace, good will to men."

Unearthly sweet in beauty, indescribably glorious in volume the song was repeated until the whole earth seemed vibrant with the sound. Over and over again the melody, so ethereal, inspiring, rapturous, fell upon their ears. Then the rushing of wings, the chorus more and more distant, and at last—silence. Long they lay there in fear and awe unspeakable. And when at last they dared to rise, the angels and the glory were gone, and the flocks and the fire were as before. But as they hurried eagerly toward Bethlehem the melody of that heavenly song had sunk deep into the sensitive soul of one, poet and musician, never to be lost. In rapture and ecstasy unspeakable, his soul swept along on the tide of that divine melody, Israfel walked toward Bethlehem, and his heart was singing the song of the angels,

"Glory to God in the highest
And on earth peace, good will to men."

They entered the stable of the inn. There on the straw was a Jewish mother and her babe. No glory shone round about them, no angelic choir sounded in that lowly place. Suddenly Israfel's mood of exaltation passed.

He had expected splendor, beauty, power, wealth. Disillusioned, the doubts and despair of yesterday, forgotten in that high hour when the angels sang, returned with redoubled force. And so, while the simple shepherds knelt in adoration before the babe at the manger, Israfel slipped out of the cave into the darkness of the night. Even the heavenly melody had little power to lighten his dark mood. Gloomy, desperate, fearful, he passed through the courtyard of the inn and out upon the highway to Jericho.

⚹ ⚹ ⚹

Fifty years have gone by since the angel's song sounded over Bethlehem's plains, and along a narrow street in the poorer quarter of Rome stumbles a man, ragged, old, broken, weary, carrying in one arm a battered lyre. There is little likeness to the beautiful young singer who once led the temple worshippers in the music of the psalms, yet this pitiful figure is none other than Israfel, son of Simeon. A half-century of wandering from city to city—Antioch, Ephesus, Lydda, Corinth, Syracuse—has finally brought him to the metropolis of the Roman Empire. Cut off from fellowship with his nation by the mighty ban of the Jerusalem Church, embittered by scorn and hatred from his own people, he had turned Greek and had sought to sever his connection with the past and conceal his identity under a Greek name. Seeking a livelihood, his ability as a singer had soon found him a welcome, and no longer in temple or synagogue, but in festal chamber, in silken boudoir, in private garden, the talents of Apelles the Troubadour made him the favorite singer of his day. Song after song he composed, love-ballads, martial odes, hero-epics, drinking-songs, until he found fame and wealth his own. But the soft temptations of this new life, the hours of dissipation and license had their inevitable effect. At last his wealth was gone, his strength began to fail, his youthful beauty faded, his wondrous voice retained only the shadow of its former glory; and he lived from hand to mouth for years, eking out an existence by playing his harp in the wine-shops and dives of the great cities, where more than once he heard the drinking-songs he had composed shouted by the convivial spirits in drunken chorus. And now he had just been refused admission to the wine-shop at the end of the street; and he was cold, and hungry, and desperate. As he passed by a house that stood a little back from the street, the sound of singing arrested him. Listening, he caught the refrain,

"O praise the Lord; for He is good;
For His mercy endureth forever!"

It was the Hallel, the old Passover hymn of his youth. Strange, this was not the Passover season! Could these be Jews? If so, he would pass on, for he had experienced enough of their harshness and scorn. But, hark, they were singing again a rude chant.

"O gladsome light of the Father immortal,
And of the celestial, saved and blessed,
Jesus our Savior! Jesus our Savior!
Now be Thou exalted!"

"Jesus! Jesus!" He groped in his dull brain for the meaning. Ah, now he remembered! One Jesus had been crucified in Jerusalem. He remembered that he had heard of it at Ephesus, and of the new religion of those that believed in Him. So these were Christians, and this was a Christian hymn! He made as if to pass on, but some impulse bade him go in. A moment he hesitated, then thrust open the door and entered. He stood in a large room. At the farther end on a raised platform was a table spread as for the Paschal feast with bread and wine, and standing behind it a stalwart, bearded man, who gazed gravely at Israfel as he entered, then motioned him to come forward and be seated. Dazed and bewildered by the kindness of his reception, Israfel sank into a vacant seat. And then the leader began to speak. He told of his life as a fisherman of Galilee; of how one day a stranger called him from his nets and he obeyed the will of that great personality; pictured the healing of the sick, blind, maimed, lepers, by this new Master; repeated the wondrous words He spoke; told of the hour on the mount when He was transfigured before them; then with hushed voice, while men hung on his every word, he told the old, old story of the cross and the love of Jesus Christ for men.

And then he said, "This is His Passover. To this table He invites all who believe in Him. No one is too sinful to come." And with bowed head and tears streaming down his cheeks he told the story of how he had denied his Master and of that hour by Galilee when he had been forgiven. Then, stretching out his hands in invitation, Peter cried to the congregation, "Come and find Him who is your Savior. He will not turn away from any repentant sinner. Will you not come?" Tearfully Israfel looked up into Peter's eyes. And at the beckoning hand he came forward and fell on his knees and as the great apostle offered up prayer for this penitent soul, all the hardness, bitterness, the sin of those many years fell away and the heart of Israfel was as the heart of a little child. Again had Christ's miracle of transformation been wrought in a human soul.

⚹ ⚹ ⚹

In the warmth, the geniality, the kindness of this Christian fellowship, the broken spirit of Israfel began to revive. The old lassitude and hopelessness gave place to an eager desire for service. Humbly he begged that he might have his share in the work of the church at Rome. And as little by little his self-respect and confidence returned he gathered about him the younger members of the church, and with the ripe knowledge of those many years he trained them to lead in the ministry of song. And as, lyre in hand, Israfel led his chorus in the psalms and simple hymns of the Christian church he found a happiness he had not known in years, and peace came to dwell in his heart.

The years passed swiftly by, and Israfel abode in the church at Rome. His spirit stirred by the mystery and beauty of the Christian faith, the old creative genius revived again. Song after song he composed, "spiritual songs" he called them; filled with the beauty of Grecian music he had learned so well to know; and the dignity and fervor of those far-off days when Hebrew music was his all in all; but instinct with a new power and passion that were neither Hebrew nor Greek, but the product of love for and fellowship with the Christ. So simple, so melodious, so inspiring, were those "spiritual songs" that they were carried from Rome to Ephesus, to Colossae, to Corinth, to Philippi, where they brought help and new strength to Christian hearts. Again and again had the memory of that wonderful night when the angels sang returned now to Israfel, but search as he might in his memory, the ethereal melody of that heavenly choir forever eluded his grasp. And ever eagerly he longed that some day he might find and give to the church that divine song, as his last gift to the cause of his Master. And so he prayed and waited.

✣ ✣ ✣

Ten years had passed by since Israfel had first heard the story of the Christ. And now there fell on the church the mailed hands of Rome. Nero, insensate and bestial, had turned the anger of Rome against the Christians, and the church at Rome met the first blast of the imperial wrath. Driven from their homes, slain by the sword, burned as living torches in Nero's gardens, the little church, broken and decimated, but undismayed, took refuge in the catacombs. Secretly and by night (for spies and enemies were everywhere), the church had met in an underground funeral crypt, in this home of the dead, to celebrate the Eucharist. There was great joy in the hearts of the brethren despite their desperate plight; for Luke, the physician and friend of Paul, was this night to read to them his newly-written story of the Master's life. As they gathered in the torchlight they listened with rapt hearts as the reader opened the scroll and began to read. And as he told the story of Mary and Joseph, of the birth of Jesus, of the shepherds and the vision, of the words of the angel, Israfel leaned his aged head upon his lyre while a flood of memories swept over his soul. Again he was a lad among those shepherds, again he awoke to the glory and the angelic message, and as the reader reached the words of the angel-song, a low cry of rapture turned the startled gaze of the church toward Israfel. Sweeping his fingers over the lyre, in a voice broken at first, but gaining again its youthful power and sweetness, he began to sing,

> "Glory to God in the highest,
> And on earth peace, good will to men!"

It was the music of the angelic chorus that sounded on the ears of the little church of Rome. Rapt in ecstasy, his face lifted to heaven, Israfel sang on and on, while men listened in awe and wonder to the divinely beautiful melody. Swept along on the wings of song, first one and then another voice took up the strain, until the whole congregation made the vaulted roof to ring with the song that once the angels sang. Recking not of spies and secrecy, caring not for danger or death, over and over they sang,

> "Glory to God in the highest,
> And on earth peace, good will to men."

A passing Roman sentry halted, listened, whistled shrilly, and the next instant the door of the secret crypt was battered down and the Roman soldiery rushed in.

✣ ✣ ✣

The weary weeks passed by. Languishing in the dungeons of the Coliseum, the Christians waited their doom. During those long days of despair and waiting, one thought had brought chiefest distress to Israfel—that the song of the angels carried in his heart so many years must die; must perish with those who had heard it but the once. And his heart was sad that this his greatest song must be forever lost. But at last word came that the end was at hand; on the morrow they must die. And that night Israfel had a dream. He thought that in spirit he was carried on through the coming years into great cities and strange lands. He stood in great cathedrals and heard the multitudes lift their voices in the "Amen" and "Kyrie." He sat in vast music halls and heard the mighty choruses of composers yet-to-be. He entered enormous tabernacles and listened to gospel songs that stirred the hearts of men. He stood by the sick, in the home, in the streets and heard echoes everywhere of the songs in praise of Christ. And in all these anthems and masses, these oratorios and choruses, these hymns and songs, one refrain repeated itself again and again. It was the music of his angel song. He awoke strangely comforted. Surely it was a message from God to assure him that his song was immortal, that it could never die.

✣ ✣ ✣

The next day the doors of the prison opened and the Roman guards stood before them, bidding them to arise and go unto death. Out into the vast amphitheatre stepped the little band of Christians, marching unfalteringly to their doom. In silence they passed to the center of the arena amid the hisses and outcries of the Roman populace. Suddenly the old man who walked at the head of the procession lifted his rude crucifix and the Christians burst into song. Astonished, the multitude fell silent, as the voices of the singers rose in power and volume. Ethereal, beautiful, sweet, the melody rose and fell. No such singing had Rome ever heard as this. With faces glowing and lifted to heaven in prayer, the Christians sang on and on, while Rome marvelled,

> "Glory to God in the highest,
> And on earth peace, good will to men!"

And as Israfel looked from that vast multitude in the amphitheatre, into the faces of his beloved children and brethren of the church all alight with heaven's own glory, he clasped his hands and lifted his heart in prayer:

"O God, I thank Thee that it has been mine to keep in my heart all these years the angel-song that it might help Thy saints to die. That song shall not die, but its glory and praise shall enter into the human heart and make music in all the coming years!"

✣ ✣ ✣

There was a roar, a flash of tawny leonine forms, but still the song sounded on,

> "Glory to God in the highest,
> And on earth peace, good will to men!"

Fainter, fainter still, as one by one the Christians fell; and then silence. But Israfel the singer remained standing until the last, with eyes lifted to heaven, and on his face a smile of perfect peace.

In a Manger He Is Lying

A Polish Carol

1. In a man-ger He is ly-ing, Who will run to greet Him there?
2. Dear-est In-fant, Child of Ma-ry, An-gels ho-ly sing Thy praise;

In-fant Je-sus, lit-tle Sav-ior Who His hon-or will de-clare? Come ye shep-herds,
Low-ing cat-tle, bleat-ing lamb-kins, filled with won-der stand and gaze. Sons of men, lift

gent-ly pip-ing, Play your tunes with sweet ac-cord, Make glad mu-sic for the Lord!
high your voic-es; An-gels join with full ac-cord, Sing glad hymns un-to your Lord!

Christmas is one of the most colorful Polish holidays. It begins on "Wigilja" (December 24) and celebrations are carried through until Epiphany. Carols — "Kolendy" — are sung during this period. Poland is rich in these carols, some of them going back to the Sixteenth Century. Boys, walking with a "szopka," and attended by musicians, travel through the streets, singing carols at each house, and are rewarded with money and delicacies. A "szopka" is a puppet-theater, showing the birth of Christ and scenes of the Nativity. Usually, a large star in which a candle is burning is also carried on top of a pole.

Our carol "In a Manger He Is Lying" is a good example of the Polish carols. We can easily imagine a group of boys, gathered around a "szopka," singing these words as the scenes to which the text refers are shown to the spectators. The English words of this carol are by Cecil Cowdrey and H. N. Brobst.

Christians, · · Sing Out with Exultation

A FRENCH HYMN

1 Christ-ians sing out with ex-ul-ta-tion, And
2 In Him e-ter-nal might and pow-er To

Praise your Ben-e-fac-tor's Name! To-day the Au-thor of sal-va-tion, The
human weak-ness hath in-clined; And this poor Child brings rich-est dow-er Of

Fa-ther's well-be-lov-ed came. Of un-de-fil-ed Vir-gin Mo-ther An
gifts and grac-es to man-kind. While here His maj-es-ty dis-guis-ing, A

In-fant, all Di-vine was born, And God him-self be-came your Bro-ther Up-
ser-vant's form the Mas-ter wears Be-hold the beams of glo-ry ris-ing E'en

-on this hap-py Christ-mas morn.
from His pov-er-ty and tears.

Benedict Pictet was a pastor of the French Reformed Church in the latter half of the Seventeenth Century and was a member of the committee which was appointed by the Genevan pastors to review the new version of the Psalms in French verse by Monsieur Conrart, published in 1677. Our hymn was written by Pictet and published with others in 1705. The translation is by Henry Lascelles Jenner, 1886.

The tune is called "Navarre" and was set to Psalm 118 in the Genevan "Psalter," 1544. The composer is the famous French musician Louis Bourgeois.

3 A stable serves Him for a dwelling, And for a bed a man-ger mean; yet o'er His head, His advent telling, A new and wond'rous star is seen. Angels rehearse to men the story. The joyful story of His birth; To Him they raise the anthem: "Glory to God on high and peace on earth!"

HOLY ANGELS, TELL YOUR STORY

A RUSSIAN CAROL

1. Ho—ly an—gels Tell your sto——ry Of our Savior's won-drous birth; Let your sing—ing Still be ring——ing with its joy to all the earth!

2 Humble shepherds, Leave your pastures, Wise Men, all your treasures bring; Come before Him To adore Him, Greet with us your Lord and King!

In old Russia, Christmas was cele-brated everywhere, by young and old, rich and poor, even though there is but little trace left of it in the new Bolshevik Russia of today. An Advent season of six weeks' duration, a time of preparation, preceded Christmas. On Christmas Eve, the celebration of Christmas proper was ushered in with a long midnight church service. Christmas itself was observed for three days.

Russian Christmas songs—Kolyada —were sung in the homes and on the streets. The caroling on the streets was done in this fashion: A young maiden, dressed in white, and at-tended by others, was drawn from house to house on a sled. Whenever a stop was made the Russian carols were sung by the group.

The carol "Holy Angels, Tell Your Story" is beautiful in its childlike simplicity. The music is very appeal-ing. The English text is by the Rev. Wm. Czamanske of Sheboygan, Wis-consin.

O Gladsome Light

from the Greek

1. O glad----some light, O grace of God the Father's face,
   Th' e----ter----nal splen----dor wear----ing Ce----les----tial, ho----ly, blest,
   Our Sav----ior Je----sus Christ, Joy----ful in Thine ap----pear----ing

2. Now ere day fadeth quite, We see the evening light, Our wonted hymn outpouring; Father, of might unknown, Thee, His incarnate Son, And Holy Spirit adoring. 3. To Thee of right belongs All praise of holy songs, O Son of God, Lifegiver; Thee, therefore, O Most High, The world doth glorify. ◆◆◆◆◆ And shall exalt forever. ◆◆◆◆◆◆◆◆◆◆◆◆◆◆◆

This is one of our oldest Christian hymns. "Shepherd of Tender Youth," a paraphrase of a hymn ascribed to St. Clement of Alexandria, is perhaps older. St. Basil of Caesarea quotes this hymn in the fourth century and states that it is of ancient tradition. The original Greek title is "Phos hilaron." In the eastern churches it is still used as an evening hymn. Its text, however, is also very appropriate for Christmas. We may, in fact, call it the oldest Christmas hymn of the church, not including of course the "Gloria in excelsis" of the angels.

The English text, published in the Yattendon Hymnal in 1895, is by Robert Bridges, poet laureate of England. He had written it for his congregation at Yattendon, where he lived and worked as superintendent of music.

The tune is called "Nunc Dimittis." It was composed by Louis Bourgeois for the "Genevan Psalter," 1549. It may have been an adaptation of an existing tune, as some of its phrases are reminiscent of the old German Christmas carol, "Es ist ein Ros' entsprungen."

To Thee of right belongs all praise of holy songs

I Sing the Birth Was Born Tonight

1. I sing the birth was born to-night, The Author both of life & light; The angels so did sound it. And like the ravished shepherds said, Who saw the light and were afraid, Yet searched, & true they found it.

2. The Son of God, the eternal King, That did us all salvation bring And freed the world from danger!

He whom the whole world could not take, The Lord which heav'n & earth did make Was now laid in a manger.

3. The Father's wisdom willed it so, The Son's obedience knew no "No", Both wills were in one stature: And as that wisdom had decreed, The Word was now made flesh indeed, And took on Him our Nature.

4. What comfort by Him do we win, Who made Himself the price of sin, To make us heirs of glory! To see this Babe all innocence, A martyr born in our defense: Can man forget this story?

An English Carol

The author of this interesting Christmas song, Ben Jonson (1573-1637), is best known as a writer of plays. He was a contemporary of William Shakespeare and Sir Walter Raleigh and seems to have been on friendly terms with both. His plays include "Every Man in His Humor," "Every Man Out of His Humor," "The Tale of a Tub," etc. He is known as a hymn-writer mainly through this carol. He was made poet laureate in 1619. He is buried in Westminster Abbey. This carol was published with Jonson's other works in 1640, bearing the title "A Hymn on the Nativity of My Savior."

The tune is known as Old 113th or Innocents and was set to the 113th Psalm in the "Four-score and Seven Psalmes," 1561. It is based on an old German tune. The arrangement is by H. E. Wooldridge.

All Praise to Thee, Eternal God

A GERMAN CAROL

1. All praise to Thee, E-tern-al God, Who wore the garb of flesh & blood; And chose a man-ger for Thy throne, While worlds on worlds were Thine a-lone. Hal-le-lu-jah!

2. Once did the skies before Thee bow;
A Virgin's arms contain Thee now;
While angels who in Thee rejoice
Now listen for Thy infant voice.
H·A·L·L·E·L·U·J·A·H!!

3. A little Child! Thou art our Guest,
That weary ones in Thee may rest;
Forlorn and lowly is Thy birth,
That we may rise to heaven from earth.
····H·A·L·L·E·L·U·J·A·H!!···

4. Thou comest in the darksome night,
To make us children of the light,
To make us in the realms divine,
Like Thine own angels; round Thee shine.
H·A·L·L·E·L·U·J·A·H·!!

5. All this for us Thy love hath done;
By this to Thee our love is won;
For this our joyful songs we raise
And shout our thanks in ceaseless praise.
H·A·L·L·E·L·U·J·A·H!!

This hymn, from the pen of Martin Luther, was first published in 1524 and has the distinction of being the first of the innumerable Christmas songs and carols produced by evangelical Christendom. The first stanza is based on an earlier German stanza, probably of the fourteenth century, based on a Latin sequence of the eleventh century. The melody is most likely also of pre-Reformation origin, but it was set to Luther's words by his friend and co-worker, Johann Walther. The translator is unknown.

Count Ludwig von Zinzendorf, the great organizer of the Moravian missions, had the privilege of hearing this hymn sung by heathen converts. It was in the year 1738. The Count had come across the Atlantic to investigate certain difficulties which were hindering the Moravian missionaries on the Island of St. Thomas. He was able to settle the trouble. Then he stayed on the island a little longer and preached the Gospel to the negroes with marked success. One day he heard them confess their faith in Christ and afterwards they joined in the singing of this hymn.

Christ the Lord to Us Is Born, Hallelujah!

Bohemian CAROL

This jubilant Christmas hymn, "Christ the Lord to Us Is Born," comes to us from the Bohemian. Juraj Tranovsky, who was for Slovak hymnody what Luther was for German hymnody, included this hymn in the first edition of his "Tranoscius," 1636. The author is unknown. Tobias Zavorka included this hymn in his collection of 1602. The translator of stanzas 1-4 was Vincent Pizek, the pastor of a Bohemian congregation in New York, the "John Hus Presbyterian Church." He died about ten years ago. The translator of stanzas five and six is John Bajus, pastor of St. John's Church in Granite City, Illinois.

The tune is of fifteenth century origin. The composer is unknown. It is called "Salvator Natus."

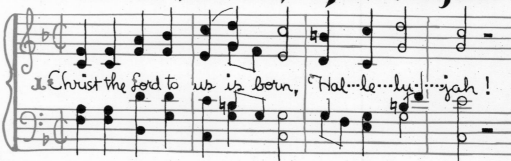

1. Christ the Lord to us is born, Hal-le-lu-jah!

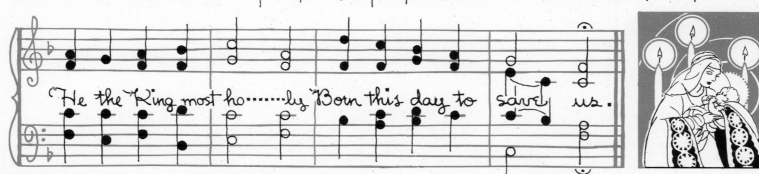

On this joy-ous Christmas morn, Hal-le-lu-jah! Of a vir-gin low-ly.

He the King most ho-ly Born this day to save us.

2 Prophesied in days of old, Hallelujah! God has sent Him as foretold, Hallelujah! Of a virgin lowly He the King most holy, Born this day to save us. 5 Grace Divine, be with us still, Hallelujah! Keep us from all harm & ill, Hallelujah! For the sake of Jesus, Who from sin now saves us, Grant to us Thy mercy.

Now Found Is The Fairest of Roses

DANISH CAROL

Now found is the Fair-est of Ros-es, Its a
beaut-y 'mong thorns it dis-clos-es; This Rose, seen in Shar-on's fair
mea-dow Is Je-sus 'mong men in death's sha-dow.

2 Since sin of God's image bereft us, No glory or merit was left us, We, strip't of our fairest possessions, Were dead in our sins and transgressions. 3 But God in his mercy would save us; A rose full of fragrance He gave us; It made of the desert a garden, By bring:ing to us life and pardon. 4 Now blossoms the Church through Its merit to bring forth the fruit of the Spirit, For Jesus her growth e'er doth nour:ish, In Him she doth live & doth flourish.

6 O Jesus, I ever adore Thee, My Rose, and my Crown and my Glory. Thou wholly my heart art possess:ing, Thy sweetness is fullness of blessing

Bishop Brorson & Christian VI

This is a Christmas song that comes to us from the land of Denmark. Hans Adolf Brorson (1694-1764), the author, was one of the greatest hymn-writers produced by that country. His poetical gifts won for him the favor of his king. The story goes that the Danish ruler, Christian VI, in the course of a conversation once asked Brorson, who was the Lutheran minister of Ribe at the time, whether he had written a certain hymn which was a favorite of the king's. Brorson admitted his authorship, and the king then and there promised him a bishopric. Thus Brorson became Lutheran bishop of Ribe and filled that position creditably until his death. As bishop of Ribe he had the honor afterwards of preaching the sermon at the funeral of Christian VI.

Bishop Brorson wrote many hymns. His Christmas hymns especially are praised very highly. One biographer writes: "No one has before or since sung in such a manner concerning Christmas."

Our hymn was written in 1732. The English version is by the Rev. Mr. C. Doving of Chicago, one of the outstanding authorities on hymnology in America. It was written in 1914.

23

NEW ENGLAND

AT THE WINDOW PANE   24

25

IT'S A HOLIDAY

© Philip Gendre

27

WHITE FIELDS

© *Philip Gendreau*

R. F. D.   28

YOSEMITE

DECEMBER

The White Shawl

BY ESTHER CHAPMAN ROBB

Illustrated by Edward Clusin

OUT of the long silence, cold and smothering as the snow-storm itself, Laurel asked, "Are we here?" and rubbed impatiently with her small gloved hand at the misted car window.

"Right," said Stephen, relieved that she had spoken, but uncertain as to how to reach her remoteness with words. Words—always the wrong ones—there had been far too many of them already. Through the arc which the windshield wiper had labored to keep clear for him all the long drive from the city, he watched the white road slanting steeply down to the long-pointed stars in the snow which were the lights of Glen Mills.

"Four hours of it," he said unhappily. "I wish we—I wish I hadn't come. I ought to have taken the train from St. Paul as I planned in the first place."

"And leave me to break it all alone?" Laurel demanded.

"You'll know how to put it; I won't. What a sour note for Christmas Eve! Well—guess I'll stop by Lindstrom's and tell Pete to come for me by ten of eleven—"

"But of course I'll drive you down," she said quickly.

"No, thanks. I'll say goodbye to you at the house."

"As you like," she returned, lifting her chin slightly. "Have you any objection to taking the car yourself, and leaving it at the station?"

"I have. It's *your* car, and you'll need it tomorrow."

"It's your car just as much as it is mine!"

Because there was a break in her voice, Stephen said brusquely, "Let's not go over that again. Well . . . . shall we stop downtown and get a bite? It's late, and your father likes his dinner early."

"That would hurt Grace's feelings; she'll have kept something hot for us."

"Just as you say." The next words came out before he could call them back: "It won't be the same without your mother."

"No," said Laurel in a low, tense voice, "Christmas will never be the same again."

Christmas was the one thing Laurel allowed herself to be sentimental about, Stephen reminded himself. When

32

her sister's letter had come proposing Christmas as usual, she had agreed that mother would wish it so, that father would be looking for them all. Resisting the well-meant efforts of his children to dislodge him, Mr. Dean insisted upon fending for himself in the old house, with the occasional heavy-handed ministrations of Grace Bloomberg. Grace would do her devoted best, but Stephen was convinced that this attempt at a family Christmas would be a painful experience for them all.

He had deeply loved Laurel's gentle and gracious mother. She had treated him like one of her own sons, so that the ache of homelessness in his heart had somehow eased. It seemed to him that his own family, lost to him so early by death, would have been like the Deans; that this home was actually one he had known and loved long since. This little town, half-asleep by the river since the passing of the sawmills, reminded him that his people, too, had been builders of the West. To such a frontier as this, had trekked his pioneering great-grandfather to keep store....

At the state university, where his guardian-cousin in the East had sent him because Stephen's father had graduated there, he had met and loved Laurel Dean. She was the vivid, lively type to whom "quiet" lads like him were inevitably attracted, tireless in activity and insatiable in ambition.

It hadn't been fair of him to expect that Laurel would be like her mother. She was a modern girl with a modern profession—photography. Becoming something of a vogue with her character portraits, she couldn't consider giving up her work for marriage. Stephen, trying to be modern and realistic, had given in, not anticipating how he would come to feel about it. Laurel Dean Donaldson was a personage, but Mrs. Stephen Brooks Donaldson was a young woman nobody knew.

Since boyhood his real interest had been hardware. Laurel had thought his bringing home gadgets—beet slicers, door-stops, lemon squeezers—very funny, and passed them around among their friends, saying lightly, "If I could only keep Steve out of hardware stores—" Then had come the chance to be manager of the new store the Hartwell Hardware was about to open in Willetts, North Dakota. In great excitement he tried to explain to Laurel how he felt about it. "You see, Lollie, I'll never be anything but a washout selling bonds. I never feel sure of them. I need to sell something solid over a counter. I need to live in a little place where I can chew the fat with my neighbors and look at the sky and wonder whether we'll have it clear for threshing."

Laurel had flamed, "But my work, Steve! All I've built up...."

"Lots of pictures to be taken in Dakota, Lollie. Wheat fields waving to the sky, home-places, Scandinavian farmers, wives, youngsters—"

For a moment Laurel looked as though she might be seeing all those pictures waiting to be taken. Then she brushed them away with a weary little gesture across her eyes. "But I couldn't afford to close my studio; I make...."

"Don't say, 'more than you'! It's like poison to me. I see you getting the everlasting jitters working too hard, and I'm getting them, too, watching you drive yourself, and kicking myself because I don't take better care of you. This way, with expenses down and work I know I could do, because I'd like it, I could pay all our bills myself. It would mean a lot to me."

"Don't be mid-Victorian, Steve," Laurel had said in that brittle way that was growing on her. "Of all places, North Dakota!"

"What do you really *know* about North Dakota? It's coming back fast from the dust storms. The farmers haven't bought a tool or a machine for so long that everything is broken or lost or worn out. They'll need wire and nails and paint. The wives will be asking for radios and vacuum cleaners and washing machines."

He hadn't been able to make her see that opportunity was knocking at his door. Very well, he'd go to Willetts by himself! Thinking back, he wondered how it had been possible for two who loved each other to say such two-edged and bitter things. All their bridges were burned—except one. There remained only the task of telling the family.

When the Hartwell Company had asked him how soon he could go out to Willetts, he had told them, "Immediately." No, he didn't care about waiting until after Christmas. Then Laurel had asked him, as a favor, to go to Glen Mills with her for Christmas Eve, pleading that the explanations she would have to make for his absence would add too heavy a burden to a holiday that would be difficult enough. If Steve were present, even for four hours, the break wouldn't seem so final.

From Lindstrom's little shack by the river, they climbed the bluff again to the older residence section. At the corner of Maple and St. Croix, a rambling white house with a narrow, slender-columned porch cast rectangles of yellow light upon the snow. The bridal-wreath bushes were bending low with a heavier bloom than they had borne in May. The walk to the front door had been recently shoveled clean, but it was filling in again rapidly.

"The boys used to groan because we lived on the corner, and they had to shovel both walks," Laurel remembered audibly. As they scraped their snow-packed feet on the wire mat, the door popped open, and Stephen and Laurel were suddenly in the warm, bright hall under the prismed chandelier. There was the fragrance of coffee, and a confusion of welcoming voices, subdued from the hilarious shouts of other years.

Mr. Dean, his white hair a little long over the velvet collar of his dressing-jacket, his eyes bright brown under brushy white brows, came forward with quiet satisfaction. "Lollie! Steve! I told them you'd make it! Radio says the driving's bad, but I knew a little old-fashioned Minnesota weather couldn't keep you from coming home for Christmas."

Laurel kissed the cheek he stooped to give her, then turned abruptly to the far end of the hall. Laying her modish little hat on the marble shelf of the walnut hat rack, she stood there for a moment before the mirror, pushing up the russet waves of her hair. Eyes, lashes, brows were all of the same vibrant shade, very lovely against the creamy pallor of her skin. "Too pale tonight," thought Stephen, and followed her quick, seeking glance into the sitting room. It traveled over the homely clutter of Victorian and Mission pieces until it found a brown wicker rocker. Over the high back of this chair lay a folded square of white wool. Laurel caught her lower lip briefly, then turned to join the family.

Suddenly, with creaking jerks, the double doors of the dining room were pulled apart, and there stood Grace Bloomberg, a durable-looking woman of more than middle age. Beaming and nodding, she wiped her red hands on her white apron, and held out first the left and then the right in awkward welcome.

"I wouldn't dish up till you come, Lollie," she said with her high-pitched, apologetic giggle. "Ain't it the limit how I can't never remember to say, 'Dinner's served,' like you learned me? Anyway, 'sall on!"

With all its extra leaves inserted, the table stretched the length of the wood-paneled dining room. Mr. Dean, at the head, lifted dish covers and pronounced, "Good: baked potatoes and dried beef gravy. You can't beat that combination. You were all raised on it." Then, with a glance at the closed door into the kitchen, he added, "Well, Grace does her best, but no one can make dried beef gravy as your mother could."

"She always frizzled it in plenty of butter first," sister Helen said from mother's place. Then, flushing because she had spoken so matter-of-factly, she bowed her head quickly, pressing a hand on the child seated on either side of her to insure quiet while grandfather asked the blessing.

"Still the priest in his own household," thought Stephen, only half-hearing the familiar, sonorous words of the grace: "Bless this food to our use and us to Thy service."

There were six children at table. Helen and Albert Tupper had four: Jessie, a solemn-eyed little girl with long brown braids; Edward, a snub-nosed lad with a gap in his front teeth; David and Jonathan, the four-year-old twins who could not be trusted to sit together. Norman Dean and his shy Swedish wife, Inga, had beaten the snowstorm down from Duluth. Their eldest, Carl, blue-eyed and flaxen-haired, sat high on the old Webster's Dictionary, while the fourteen-months baby girl occupied the highchair and busily plastered her fat pink cheeks with cereal.

After dinner Helen offered to help Inga get her babies to bed, remaining upstairs to make up the cots mother had bought for Laurel's house parties and kept to be ready for the visits of the grandchildren. In the sheer black dress into which she had changed for the evening, Laurel gathered the other children around her and read to them "The Birds' Christmas Carol." The turbulent twins ceased their puppyish wrestling on the worn carpet, and edged closer until they were leaning against her knees. Edward lay on his stomach at her feet, chin cupped in his stubby hands. Stephen, watching them from across the sitting room, saw Laurel's arm in its long, graceful sleeve reach out to draw in self-conscious little Jessie. It was a pity, he felt sharply, that there was no place in Laurel's crowded life for children of her own. She would have loved them. . . . .

Closing the book now, Laurel cried gaily enough, "To bed with you, darlings! Just think, Jessie, next Christmas, when you're twelve, you will be allowed to join the trimmers of the tree."

With the children safely out of the way, there was feverish activity in the sitting room. The tree had to be dragged in from the back porch and shaken free of snow; the tree-stand had to be brought up from the basement; the attic ransacked for the boxes of trimmings; the linen closet turned out for a sufficiently worn sheet. Of all such details sister Helen was in command. Tirelessly she ran upstairs and down, protesting that it would help her "reduce," and holding up a warning finger to remind loud talkers that there were sleeping babies.

At the quieter end of the room, Stephen talked with Albert Tupper, a plain, thick-set man with sandy hair and kindly, shrewd face. Sure of Steve's interest, Al drew out a catalog and began to show him the new line of farm tools he was adding to his stock at the Tupper Hardware on Main Street.

Feeling Laurel's eyes upon him as he turned the pages, Stephen looked up and read her anxious speculation as to whether he would tell Al Tupper about the store in Willetts, North Dakota. He thought her slight frown and the tight line of her mouth meant, "Not yet," and he nodded imperceptibly to show her that he understood perfectly. By ten-thirty, at the latest, he had figured, it would have to come out.

"Oh, say, folks!" exclaimed Al, his homely face contrite. "If I didn't forget to bring home those new electric lights for the tree! Had them all laid out on the counter. I'll just run down to the store and get them—only take a minute. Maybe Steve will go with me."

"Oh, no, don't, Al," said Laurel. "I'm glad you forgot them. We can use candles again. Here's a whole box. And here are the big ones to put in the windows."

"Yes, have everything the way mother had it," urged Mr. Dean, leaning forward in his Morris chair by the secretary. "I've been wanting to tell you all something. You're making a great mistake to talk all around her the way you've been doing. When Helen said a nice, normal thing about mother's dried beef gravy, she looked as if she'd made a break of some kind. You're running around here making a clatter to keep from thinking about her. That isn't right. Think about her! Talk about her! When you're old and alone, you'll know what I know: no one dies as long as love remembers."

There was a moment of silence, rich with recognition, in the Christmas-cluttered room. Laurel spoke first. Reaching out her hand to the brown wicker rocker and laying it like a caress on the folded white square, she said softly, "Mother's shawl. She left it there when she went into the other room."

"'The other room,'" said Mr. Dean eagerly, "that's how I think of it. Lollie, I remember when I bought that shawl for her—when Norman was a baby. She liked the feel of it about her shoulders—light, but warm. Last winter she got it out again and kept it on her chair."

"Norm! Do you see this gap in the fringe? That's where *you* hacked it out with the kitchen scissors, to make yourself a Rip Van Winkle beard."

"I ought to have been spanked all right, but what I remember is how mother laughed when she came to our show in the barn."

Helen, on her knees before the cardboard boxes, held up a shapeless bit of black flannel and peanuts.

"The Peanut Man!" exclaimed Mr. Dean, taking it in his hand and turning it over thoughtfully. "When you were babies, Mrs. Parker, our next-door neighbor, made it for our tree. It was a Chinaman with a long queue down his back—quite a dignified fellow. On Christmas Eve the neighbors used to visit all the trees in the block and take some little thing for the trimming. It was a nice custom. Mother started it."

"See that scorched spot on his coat?" Norman pointed out. "Remember mother's story about that? She said, when a twig caught fire from a short candle, the Peanut

Man swung and twisted on his cord until he broke it so that he could fall on the fire and put it out for us."

"And *you* said," Helen added, " 'Huh, his string burned and he had to fall.' " And then mother said, " 'Let's give him the benefit of the doubt. Always expect the best from everyone.' "

Mr. Dean showed Inga the gold star he held in his hand, then passed it up to Laurel, who had mounted the step ladder. "Here, Lollie, don't forget the star for the tip. Mother made it. She was always making pretty things."

"Didn't she use to paint a little, father?"

"More than a little. She graduated from the Art School in Cincinnati, and opened a little studio of her own to give lessons. She had it only a year, because we were married then, and I wanted to go back West to take over the paper when it got too much for your grandfather."

"Why she never told me that!" said Laurel. "I never dreamed she was professional."

"It must have slipped her mind. She was always pretty busy."

When the tree was decked to everyone's satisfaction, Stephen stole a look at his watch. It was past ten. Was Laurel leaving it to him after all? Still, there had been no suitable moment to broach the matter. He tried to catch her eyes, but she would not look his way. Into his anxiety and indecision came Helen's kind voice: "Poor Steve, we gabby Deans haven't given you a chance to get a word in edgewise. Tell us about some Christmas you remember."

Stephen could only stammer in confusion. "Well . . . . you know I hadn't any real home. I remember—that time your mother asked me to spend my Christmas vacation here. The last night the tree was to be up,—I remember—Lollie and I came in late from a party, and she lighted the candles for me once more, and somehow, there by the tree we knew . . . . well, Christmas always means Lollie to me."

Appalled at this intimate revelation before them all, he broke off, half expecting to hear Laurel's "Don't be sentimental, Steve." But her face was turned away from him. There was something tense in the slant of her red-brown head. Maybe she'd like it if he left the room and gave her a clear field. He stood up decisively, saying with a brisk change of tone, "Guess I'll go out to the kitchen to have a visit with Grace. I hear her still thumping around out there, and I promised her I'd see if I could fix the ice-box leak. By the way, Helen, is she still engaged to her old faithful, the ice-man with the Chester A. Arthur whiskers?"

Helen laughed. "The status quo is unchanged. She'll neither set the day nor give him up altogether. She has a queer complex about divorce. Having read that every sixth marriage ends in divorce, she fears hers might be the inevitable sixth that goes on the rocks. As if it were a matter of statistics, and not clashing wills."

As Stephen went to the kitchen, Mr. Dean arose, winding his watch suggestively. When Stephen came back, only Laurel was in the sitting room, moving restlessly about, stooping now and then to pick a bit of tinsel from the rug.

"They've all gone to bed to get some sleep before the children begin in the morning," she said, not looking at him.

"Oh! Well—then you'll have to make my goodbyes for me in the morning. What do you think old Grace said to me?"

"I haven't a notion."

"She's invited us—you and me—to come to her wedding New Year's Day. Her mind's made up at last. And by what? By observing the marital bliss of the Deans. She said, 'When I see how happy you all are, with every man for his wife, and every woman for her husband—and not even death big enough to separate you, I know I'm a timid old fool to miss out on fourteen years of lovin'.' "

"Don't laugh," said Laurel tensely. "It isn't funny."

"You must admit it has its humorous aspect. Though I grant you, in view of the situation, it has a certain element of pathos."

"Don't talk that silly, stilted way! I—I can't bear it."

Taut as a rubber binder stretched too thin, she reproached him: "Now I've got to take the brunt of it all alone—on Christmas morning."

"Oh! Then you didn't tell them? I understood you were going to find a time to break it gently."

"Then why did you make it impossible for me by telling that—about the tree and us? Oh, well, let it go . . . . Pete will be here for you any minute."

"Lollie," said Stephen gently, noting how white and strained she looked, "will you do something for me? Will you light the tree?"

"No," she said. "I—I won't."

With cool decision she put down the candle he held out to her.

At that Stephen's own nerves seemed to snap. "All right—all right," he heard himself biting off the words between his teeth. "I'm going to treat you as your mother did when you were naughty. I'm going to spank you."

As he reached for her, she stepped back, furious at him. The sleeve of her sheer dress swung past the candle. There was a blaze, bright and terrible as the face of sudden death. Horror gripped Stephen, but love set him free to act swiftly. He leaped at the brown rocker, snatched the white wool shawl, wrapped her close. Tight against his breast he held her in an unbearable agony of fear and deep, protective passion. She trembled violently, and then, relaxing, began to sob in long, shuddering gasps of terror and release.

"Oh, Lollie, darling, darling," he besought her, "forgive me! I was a beast to you! I'm afraid to look—to see whether you're horribly burned . . . . "

"No, Steve, no, I'm not—because you were so quick to save me. See, Steve, it's only a little red. Oh, Steve, mother's shawl was there!"

"Where she left it for us, Lollie."

"It gives a lovely light," she repeated to herself.

"I don't understand . . . . "

"There's something about the shawl. Oh, I know I don't sound rational. But I am, really, Steve. I mean something about her life still shining—a lovely light. I couldn't tell them about us, Steve, because I saw—I hoped—that our children would keep *me* living with the remembrance of little things."

His arms tightened about her, and, through tears, she smiled at him. Then, suddenly alert, she lifted her head from his shoulder and asked, "What time is it?"

"No matter. Just past eleven, I think."

"You'll miss the train. Why, Pete didn't come!"

"When I was in the kitchen, I phoned him not to. I'll wire in the morning that I've changed my mind. How can I go, Lollie?"

Laurel's still-wet eyes brightened with purpose. "Steve, that train waits a half hour in St. Paul. We can catch it, if we take the new cut-off. Quick, help me tie up my arm, and I'll change into a warm dress. This sleeve's a wreck."

"Lollie, you don't mean. . . ."

"I'm going with you! O Steve, I've tried so hard not to give in—to be a modern woman. Smart. Self-sufficient. But I can't be hard—because I've got a weak spot. For you, Steve. And I'm the one who's been a beast to you."

"I'm ashamed of that," he said contritely. "Don't ever remind me I tried to. . . ."

"Give me a spanking? Well, I had it coming, darling!"

Her arms tightened around him then, and her red-brown head rested on his shoulder again, close against his chin. "Just an old-fashioned wife who can't do without her husband."

"But the family, Lollie," Stephen suddenly remembered. "I can't take you away without a word like this. Perhaps you ought to come later. . . ."

"Please, Steve, right now. There's nothing like getting a good start on a new job. I can come back for a few days to close my studio. Grace is still up; she'll love to have news to tell in the morning. They'll understand. This is marriage, Steve, and we've—I've—never even tried it."

It had stopped snowing now, and a high moon, misted with a shining aureole, made glorious a new white world. Stephen pressed the starter. "Wait a minute," cried Laurel. "There's Grace on the porch, with her head all tied up. She's waving goodbye like mad. I forgot to wish her. . . ."

She stepped down into a snowdrift and floundered back to the house. Impulsively she kissed the rough, cold cheek, wet with tears of true sentiment.

"I'm sorry we must miss your wedding, Grace, dear. All our best wishes for your happiness."

"And I'm tellin' you, Lollie, with your example plain before me as the nose on my face, I'd be a loony if I couldn't hit it off with Gus. You just back 'em up good, ain't that about the size of it?"

Laurel laughed, "It's the old reliable recipe, Grace. Goodbye! Happy days! And merry Christmas!"

The Leaden Army Conquers the World

BY ADALBERT R. KRETZMANN

GREAT presses roared up through the Holy Night. John, the night foreman, walked around the gallery over the rolling giants that were grinding out tomorrow's reading for two million subscribers. As the folded papers foamed up the bands to the loading platform he focused his eyes on the headline. Did they break the line he had set for the fortieth year or did that newsflash about the brutal bombers hitting the crowded Christmas Eve Church in Boremont take it out? No, it was still there—his line—*"Peace on earth, good will to men."* Almost tears in it this year: "Peace"—not panic; "Angel wings"—not bombers; "Good will"—not the propaganda of hate; "Men"—not armored beasts of prey. He really had ideals about this when he started—printing should save the world—there should be truth in it—love—and a prayer like this one in the deep black of the Christmas headline: *"Peace on earth, good will to men."*

✐ ✐ ✐

Yes, this was the year of the Great Anniversary—printing was five hundred years old. The roar of the giant presses became a background for his thinking. He could remember the days of the hand-press. Down at the Royal Press old man Stechwald had always insisted on the proper respect for that oldest press in the shop. "That came along with me from the old country—it is over two hundred years old, but they never made a better one—only twice did I have to replace that screw." That press really had made a nice, clean imprint—real, solid, even pressure and smooth inking. High speed presses had lost that.

When the office door closed it shut out the whirr and the hum of the presses. Before him on the wall was the broadside, "The Type Speaks," designed by Frederic W. Goudy and circulated by the American Institute of Graphic Arts. He remembered his sensation of a moment ago as he stood before the beautiful, clean-cut letters.

"The Leaden Army Conquers the World." Surely this Christmastide would make everybody remember

---

THE TYPE SPEAKS

‹I AM THE VOICE OF TODAY·THE HERALD OF TOMORROW›

fwg

I AM TYPE! OF MY EARLIEST ANCESTRY NEITHER HISTORY NOR RELICS REMAIN · THE WEDGE-SHAPED SYMBOLS IMPRESSED IN PLASTIC CLAY IN THE DIM PAST BY BABYLONIAN BUILDERS FORE-SHADOWED ME · FROM THEM THROUGH THE HIEROGLYPHS OF THE ANCIENT EGYPTIANS · THE LAPIDARY INSCRIPTIONS OF THE EARLY ROMANS·DOWN TO THE BEAUTIFUL LETTERS BY THE SCRIBES OF THE ITALIAN RENAISSANCE · I WAS IN THE MAKING

JOHN GUTENBERG

WAS THE FIRST TO CAST ME IN METAL · FROM HIS CHANCE THOUGHT STRAYING THROUGH AN IDLE REVERIE—A DREAM MOST GOLDEN · THE PROFOUND ART OF PRINTING WITH MOV-ABLE TYPES WAS BORN · COLD · RIGID · IMPLACABLE I MAY BE · YET THE FIRST IMPRESS OF MY FACE BROUGHT THE DIVINE WORD TO COUNTLESS THOUSANDS · I BRING INTO THE LIGHT OF DAY THE PRECIOUS STORES OF KNOWLEDGE & WISDOM LONG HIDDEN IN THE GRAVE OF IGNORANCE ·
I COIN FOR YOU THE ENCHANTING TALE · THE PHILOSOPHER'S MORALIZING AND THE POET'S VISIONS · I ENABLE YOU TO EX-CHANGE THE IRKSOME HOURS THAT COME · AT TIMES · TO EVERY ONE · FOR SWEET AND HAPPY HOURS WITH BOOKS—GOLDEN URNS FILLED WITH ALL THE MANNA OF THE PAST · IN BOOKS I PRESENT A PORTION OF THE ETERNAL MIND CAUGHT IN ITS PROGRESS THROUGH THE WORLD · STAMPED IN AN INSTANT & PRESERVED FOR ETERNITY · THROUGH ME · SOCRATES AND PLATO · CHAUCER AND THE BARDS BECOME YOUR FAITHFUL FRIENDS WHO EVER SURROUND AND MINISTER TO YOU · I AM THE LEADEN ARMY THAT CONQUERS THE WORLD—
I AM TYPE!

---

that back in 1439 and 1440 —just five hundred years ago—men were painstakingly laying the foundation for the speed and the roar of the giant presses outside his door. Last year he had heard them tell about the famous Freeman's Oath and an Almanac, both issued back in 1639, from the Stephen Daye Press at Cambridge, Massachusetts, but no one had ever seen a copy of those. Most likely they would center their celebration this year on "Bay Psalm Book," printed in 1640, and of which eleven copies still existed.

✐ ✐ ✐

The call bell tapped out its hoarse twelve strokes— midnight, and the dawn of Christmas Day was beginning to creep up over the war-scarred, blood-stained fields of western Europe. The Rhine Valley, scene of so many triumphs for the arts and sciences, bore its marks, too. Somehow one longed to get back to those other days when life moved more peaceably and a man had a chance to tend to his work. It was true that there were many other things to discourage achievement, many other hardships to overcome, but in those days they lay more in nature than in man. Great names were written into the history of the valley. There was Martin Schongauer of Colmar, the best painter and engraver of his time, and Diebold Lauber of Hagenau, a really great book illustrator; but the headquarters for the whole cultural group was in Mainz. From 1326 to the year 1500, however, seventy-two waves of pestilence swept through the city. Small wonder that Gutenberg left the city for twelve years and did the actual work of experimentation in the city of Strassburg.

✐ ✐ ✐

Back in 1925, the Printing House Craftsmen had sent John to Mainz as their representative at the twenty-fifth anniversary of the Gutenberg Museum. The fact that it was Christmas Day now recalled to his mind that on Christmas Day in 1438, Andreas Dritzehn, an artisan trained in many crafts, had died

JOHANN GUTENBERG

in Strassburg. John was glad that his good friend Otto Walter Fuhrmann was going to write the story of this interesting character and his relation to Gutenberg and the invention of printing. Dritzehn's death seems to have robbed him of the fruits of years of patient effort that he had confidently expected to net him a fortune. His heirs brought suit during the year 1439 against the partnership headed by one Johann Gutenberg. The results of the suit surely could no longer be important, but as John now recalled the facts they, at least, showed very certainly that this Johann Gutenberg had invented a method of casting type. How grateful the whole world could be for that. This was Christmas Day and all over the world, in more than a thousand languages, they would read the ringing words, "And it came to pass in those days that there went out a decree from Caesar Augustus . . . ." Modern civilization would hardly be possible without that. The story and the means of telling it quickly in movable type went together so beautifully and spread so rapidly that the power of Christian Missions and the possibility of lifting up the light of the Gospel once more depended, under God, almost entirely on this invention.

Over in the studio next door there were some who thought that radio was a greater invention. Let them think what they pleased. The printed word had permanence and authority. Radio and all its swift sound faded away and left no record in the ether that had transmitted it—but printing—that was different in consciousness and tempo: without it there would be nothing to preserve our history and link our generations; without it art and science could not be handed on. Printing had become the great tool of Democracy; it had made truth and beauty its companions—it had enlarged the stature of mankind—and now evil and lies had taken hold of it—but they could not take away the good and the glory of the first printed Book of books.

*   *   *

Confidently he listened to the smooth hum of the big presses in the darkness of Christmas morning. The power of that tremendous machine out there was not a mystery. It was providing swiftly and cheaply copies of what reporters and correspondents had heard and seen all over the surface of the globe. It recorded accurately what the cameras of daredevil photographers had caught on forty different news fronts. In other places those same presses were bringing forth copies of what the prophets, apostles, evangelists, poets, teachers, musicians, jurists, dramatists and jesters had written. By the steady rolling of those great cylinders and by the smooth urgency of its pressure it was bringing knowledge within the reach of every man—the creations of men's minds and spirits became common property. He had been amazed when he checked over Mortimer Adler's "How to Read a Book," and found that, of the one hundred and thirteen great books listed there, thirty-five had been written before the invention of printing. How few could then enjoy those treasures! But the printing press, Gutenberg's gift, had spent five hundred years making readers, fostering reading and guaranteeing to authors an audience and a living. It was good that in an age that had gone power mad again—where hate and steel were put to such rotten use and where lead was being moulded for bullets by the million again, one could think of a time when lead moulding made speech live after the men who had spoken.

✓ ✓ ✓

Over in the Gutenberg Museum in Mainz, Dr. Ruppel had showed him that first press and he had marveled at the fact that the hand presses of our day still worked on Gutenberg's principle although now they were of iron and steel instead of the old hard wood, and had a toggle joint instead of a screw to bring the pressure down onto the paper. Dr. Ruppel had explained to him that it had undoubtedly taken Gutenberg at least twenty years to get ready and to bring his work to perfection. Naturally, one would expect Dr. Ruppel to be a genuine sponsor of the claims of Gutenberg as the inventor of printing over against all others, but he talked very freely about Coster and Fust and Schoeffer and Sweynheym and Pannartz. His argumentation was sound all the way through. He pointed out that the claims for Gutenberg as the real inventor rested principally on three things:—

a. that Gutenberg solved all the technical problems involved in printing from movable type.
b. that Gutenberg developed his basic invention to the point where work of admirable quality could be produced—work which has not been surpassed to this day.
c. that Gutenberg's methods showed their worth because they continued in use throughout the centuries following 1440.

Dr. Ruppel had showed him an old grammar by Aelius Donatus which had been block printed—that is, the entire page cut into a block of wood. But John could see that Gothic was so hard to carve that this type of printing could never become very popular. The Chinese still persisted in this type of printing because their letters were easy to cut. Dr. Ruppel had also showed him some bronze characters which had been cut by hand by the Koreans as early as 1403, but the process was much too costly and the letters could not be cast. He then also called attention to some porcelain and wooden separate characters which had been used by the Chinese centuries ago.

At the time it seemed a rather tedious approach to the entire problem of printing from movable type, but suddenly John began to realize that there was much in the craft to which he had devoted his life about which he had never thought. He had taken for granted that the idea of having movable metal type came from the old woodcut blocks—that instead of continuing to use wood, which warped, they finally had turned to metal. Carefully Dr. Ruppel explained to him that Johann Gutenberg's mother had come from the house of Gense-

fleisch, a family of metal workers. This Gensefleisch family, according to the good doctor, belonged to the twelve families that controlled and operated the mint at Mainz. Gutenberg's uncle was master of the mint in 1428. Gutenberg was therefore familiar with the processing of metals, with engraving, punch cutting, stamping, moulding, casting, alloying, etc. From his experience as a metal worker he conceived the idea of printing from cast type faces made like coins and he did not receive the impetus from wood block technique.

In the Gutenberg Museum John had seen the moulds for the type which had been used in the famous forty-two line Bible of twelve hundred and eighty-six pages of folio size which had been issued in 1457 in two volumes. He was so fascinated by the moulds and the

FACSIMILE TYPE SPECIMEN FROM THE FORTY-TWO LINE
GUTENBERG BIBLE

type faces as they came out that he immediately made arrangements with the head of the museum to have the entire press and the moulds brought to the Century of Progress Exposition in Chicago in 1933. He realized that there would be thousands of craftsmen in America who would have the same interest in this collection.

John had to admit that up to the time that Dr. Ruppel had begun the detailed explanation of what the trick in casting was he had had no idea that all metals save two shrink at the moment of passing from the molten into the solid state. He had always taken for granted that casting a metal would automatically produce regular shapes and now the doctor was telling him that ordinary casting would not produce shapes of the required mathematical perfection. But antimony and bismuth act just like water when it freezes—they expand, and a judicious blending of these metals with lead and tin produces a mixture that answers the requirements perfectly. This alloy had to be found by hundreds of experiments and the good doctor explained that it took approximately twenty years of work to get the alloy functioning properly. He pointed out a facsimile of a statement made by Hans Duenne to the effect that he had made more than one hundred guilders' profit solely on material pertaining to printing sold to Gutenberg. John had been filled with amazement. He had read somewhere that Edison, with all the modern laboratory facilities in the world at his command, had to conduct more than three hundred experiments in search of material suitable for his lamp filaments. What a task it must have been for Gutenberg to work out chemically and with scientific accuracy an alloy which is still being used in its basic formula at the present time. Even the models, punches, lettermoulds (called matrices) were made by hand until our time. Gutenberg's development of the oil-varnish ink is still basic for printing ink and black ink is still made from linseed oil and lamp black as he made it.

✶ ✶ ✶

John still remembered very vividly the Christmas he had spent in Mainz after the celebrations at the Gutenberg Museum. Just as twilight came on the twenty-fourth he had followed a group of carolling children and as they stood opposite the Bishop's Palace he suddenly noticed that he was standing before the old Gutenberg house at the corner of "Zur Lade" and "The Christoph Strasse." Directly behind the old Gutenberg House stood the church of Saint Christopher where Johann had been baptized. When they saw that John was interested the children brought their teacher over to tell John that Johann Gutenberg had been very prompt —that each morning as the bells rang for the six o'clock mass he would hurry past the Church of St. Quentin on the way to his shop. The teacher became very enthusiastic when he pointed out that only a half mile up the street on which the printing plant stood there had been the great Church of the Franciscan Cloister where Gutenberg was buried and that over on the other side of the city was the Church of the Dominicans for which Gutenberg had originally prepared his type. This was most interesting since only the day before John had seen a copy of the Fust and Schoeffer Psalter of 1457. Now the Schoolmaster told him that the type in which that book was set had been originally prepared for missals, for books of prayers and liturgical forms in use in the churches of that period. Just when the type was ready for use the Holy See tried to standardize the missals in the various dioceses in order to avoid the confusion which was prevalent as members of the church began to move back and forth in that rapidly awakening world. In its effort to standardize these missals the Vatican forbade any to be printed until the basic missal was completed. In the meantime the huge investment of Gutenberg, Fust and Schoeffer lay idle, so they finally decided to print a Bible from the type which they had cast for missals. That accounts for the character of the type face.

✶ ✶ ✶

John had always known that the first type was made in imitation of the hand-written manuscripts of the XIV and XV century. The first books written in the West of Europe were written wholly in capitals, such as we find in inscriptions and on monuments. Then this handwriting, or, better, hand-lettering, began to assume national characteristics. France developed the Merovingian style; Italy the Lombardic; and Spain the Visigothic. Very soon they all were so involved and complicated that they were impractical. John was really thrilled to find an Emperor interesting himself in hand-lettering. Charlemagne called an internationally famous poet and writer named Alcuin to Tours from England, and asked him to establish a form of hand-lettering which should supersede all other styles. It was to be beautiful yet simple in its basic lines. From the work of Alcuin came the alphabet as we know it today, made up of capitals and small letters, and his new style spread over the world like wildfire. John's heart swelled with pride as on this Christmas morning he saw how men of all nations had worked together to bring this great gift to the Christ-child. Two other great craftsmen by the name of Sweynheym and Pannartz deserve the credit for developing Roman and so-called Italic type. John of Spires, Jenson and the two Da Spira brothers of Venice gave us the type as we know it today. Men like Caxton, Emery Walker and William Morris drew their inspiration from the beautiful clarity of the type these men developed. The New World has also added its great names to those who cast type and advanced the science of printing. But these men from the various great cultured nations of a former age will always wear the laurels of genuine achievement and highest service to mankind.

✶ ✶ ✶

"Peace on earth, good will to men"—the dawn was coming nearer over Lake Michigan and soon others would be coming in to take his place and he could go home to the family for the joy of gifts and a tree and the presence of loved ones. John made up his mind that he and the whole family were going to be at Matins this morning. The pastor would have many thoughtful things to say this year, because it seemed that real peace was so far away it only brought tears into your voice to talk about it. What could a man say—for 1900 years men had been moving forward to the frontiers of the world with this Gospel of light and peace as their gift to those who sat in darkness and in the shadow of death. Down through the years pious men sat over their writing boards and wrote as the Spirit gave them utterance and after they were gone a long company of earnest and devout men sat in their places at the smooth boards and copied what they had written, so that each church might hear the blessed Word read in the services. Little fragments were tucked into the belt of many a bewildered, persecuted follower of Jesus. By the flickering light of a torch down in the catacombs under the City of Rome they read in a whisper that carried along the tufa galleries—

"These things I command you, that ye love one another. If the world hate you, ye know that it hated me before it hated you. If ye were of the world, the world would love his own: but because ye are not of the world, but I have chosen you out of the world, therefore the world hateth you. Remember the word that I said unto you, The servant is not greater than his lord. If they have persecuted me, they will also persecute you;

if they have kept my saying, they will keep yours also. But all these things will they do unto you for my name's sake, because they know not him that sent me. If I had not come and spoken unto them, they had not had sin; but now they have no cloke for their sin. He that hateth me hateth my Father also. If I had not done among them the works which none other man did, they had not had sin: but now have they both seen and hated both me and my Father. But this cometh to pass, that the word might be fulfilled that is written in their law, They hated me without a cause. But when the Comforter is come, whom I will send unto you from the Father, even the Spirit of truth, which proceedeth from the Father, he shall testify of me: And ye also shall bear witness, because ye have been with me from the beginning."

As the centuries went on the opposition died. Love could not be resisted and held back, and suddenly those who had feared the emperor found him kneeling in their midst. Now the Word was read from costly books bound in precious leathers, studded with jewels and illuminated with real gold. Great artists labored for a lifetime over the beautiful books that are kept as heirlooms in the great churches of the East and the West and in the oratories and chapels of kings' palaces. Then the darkness came back again—the breakup of the great Roman Empire began. Men from the North who had not heard of Christ and of His love swept civilization back five hundred years and lost the arts in a welter of blood and confusion and barbarism. Only here and there within the sheltering walls of some great church men still wrote. They transcribed faithfully the words of former years in which was the wisdom of God and the salvation of men. Over the mountains through snows and blizzards they carried the precious words in pilgrims' packs. In frail little boats they brought it over to the Britons and the Celts. In the hands of young Ansgar it went up to the North and Scandinavia became the model of Christianity for all time.

✓ ✓ ✓

John wondered whether the pastor might repeat this year what he had said once before: "How fortunate you are that you can read the Christmas story—that you have this whole Gospel of the salvation through Jesus Christ in your hands. Do you know that when printing was invented seventy-five percent of the people could not even begin to appreciate this great gift because they could not read? And when Luther translated the Bible into the language of the people the greatest boon came from the fact that now the preachers could at least read to the people and they would understand, but only a few of them could really read what he had given them."

Now almost every child could have that blessing. Printing itself would be useless unless there were people who could read and the great freedom which the Reformation brought back into the world has given us modern education—an opportunity for every man to read and learn and hold fast to that which is good.

Outside it had grown strangely still. The presses had stopped. Another day's news was ready for the waiting millions.

✓ ✓ ✓

Outside the wintry night was filled with the tip-toe expectancy that belongs only to the Holy Night— the expectancy that had found an answer when the angels sang out of Judea's heavens. It was good to be going home on a night like this because home had been hallowed by the love which came down at Christmas time so long ago. As John walked over to the station he checked over the gifts—Mother, the new radio for the kitchen, so that she could follow all those stories that meant so much to her; Bob, the new set of books from the publishing house; Ruth, the skates she had wished for so long; Norman, the bicycle that had kept him awake for months; Little Joan, a new sled and fur mittens. Each was provided with a special gift, and then this one for the home—this beautiful Bible, especially bound for him by The Monastery Hill Bindery—here was truly something for the entire family. He could hardly wait. Seated on the train he undid the wrapping and held the leather lovingly in his hands—the covers were boards and on them were inlaid crosses in blood-red leather edged in gold. Inside, the print was clear and bold and black—you could feel pride of craftsmanship radiating from every line. As John turned the pages he came, quite naturally, to the Christmas story.

There it was again—just as simple and restrained and reverent as it was when Saint Luke wrote it down. Languages all over the world had been turned into print and writing only that this message might live.

The power behind the Book caught hold of John. What if men and nations had heeded the call of this great Book rather than the summons of the destroyers and devourers? What if men had any grateful remembrance for the blessings of God in nation, health and home? What if, by some miracle, the wonder of the commonplace, could be made impressive and interesting once more? What if the wonder of something very commonplace like printing should make them reflect?

This last fascinated the night foreman—surely, printing was taken too much for granted, like the air we breathe, or the heart within us. We saw too much of printing. But there it was—indispensable in the Book before him—sought after in the newspaper under his arm—teaching everything men knew or had known—giving inspiration—guiding men in the courts of law—providing sustenance for spiritual life—bringing amusement and recreation into leisure hours—reporting happenings local, national and international—supporting commerce and industry in words and pictures, in the infinite variety of printed forms, and presenting everything which contributes to success in religion, in the home, in the office, in the nation or the school so that efficiency and comfort of living were before the eyes of all.

John's thoughts went far afield—just think what volumes could be written on this Book alone—on its trials, translations, editions, preservation, oddities, beauties, etc. Multiply that by the far-reaching influence of printing in every field of human enterprise and experience—record the achievements of printing in the liberation of mankind from the bondage of ignorance and superstition—remember at every recital and concert that only printing has spread the music of the masters on the practice boards of musicians all over the world and has enabled the "universal language" to grow and prosper. Why, even the remarkable quiet hours in the playroom come from the lovely pages of the books for children which are, perhaps, the greatest blessing of this great invention.

Almost home now—the next station would be his. The work had been getting harder down at the newspaper—year after year he had told himself that this was the last year, but the fascination of the presses was too much for him. He was helping spread information and opinion—he, and those of his craft, had something great to give the world,—education, religion, music, pictures, news, laws, guidance—a man could not turn away from that lightly. Well, he would talk it over with the family once more during the coming week—and here was the station.

↙   ↙   ↙

It was odd that Bob should seem to take such a deep interest in the new Bible—but John was proud as he heard his eldest son tell Norman and Joan the story—and Bob did it well—the work at the Seminary was deepening and broadening him—but when he sat on the floor in front of the Christmas tree he was very young again and John held Mother's hand very tightly as he sensed what she was thinking: "It won't be very long now and then Bob goes out too—and we don't know where they'll place him."

"The Bible is no ordinary book. God inspired men to write it"—Bob had a pleasant voice—"Look here, at the Christmas story. Listen to it." And they did, solemnly, with the wide-open eyes of children who see past centuries and kingdoms and know exactly what the Baby Jesus looked like. "You know, they are reading this story all over the world today—in more than a thousand languages—children, black and yellow and red and white are just as happy as you are about it, and their fathers and mothers are too—and the one thing that makes Christmas possible is printing."

Bob was telling Norman and Joan about the Library of the University of Pennsylvania. Over the door are the lines:

"O blessed letters that combine in one
    All ages past, and make one line with all,
    By you do we commune with who are gone,
    And the dead-living unto counsel call."

That was the secret of it. Saint Luke was here today; "dead-living" he was telling the story. Men of every nation had to help in bringing these words down to this generation—but there Saint Luke was and there was Christmas—"living in lead" and conquering the world.

"Long, long ago the first inspired men wrote in Hebrew—that was the Old Testament. The New Testament was written in Greek. But every page had to be copied by hand. Look, how would you like to copy one thousand nine hundred and six pages? Do you think you might make a mistake and skip a word or even a line once in a while? I'll bet you would too—well, these copyists sometimes made small mistakes but when we compare other copies of the same page we usually find the mistakes and correct them.

"Even before Jesus was born there were some people who could not understand the Jewish language and so some learned Jews made a Greek translation and because seventy men worked on it they called it the Septuagint, which means seventy. Then, when the New Testament was completed in Greek, they quickly made translations into Syriac and Latin. Before Luther there were thirty-two German translations but they were all translations from the Latin and Luther and his helpers did all their work for the German Bible from the old Hebrew and Greek manuscripts. That was a tremendous piece of work but it encouraged the men in England to try new translations also. Tyndale even came to work in Wittenberg with Luther."

You could lose yourself listening to the history of the Christmas story—eighteen million copies of the Bible sold in our own country in 1939—all over the world nearly a hundred million. And the printing press had done it—books for every man, in his price-range. No one was barred. The beautiful—the educational—the legal—the musical—the religious—the amusing and the entertaining—all were at the hand of eagerness. Second-hand books could fill many needs. Long after the first buyer's hands had gone to the last rest, new and eager hands picked them up, blew the dust from the top and searched the yellowing pages for the wisdom of other days as an answer to the muddle of today.

After a day like this a man felt like working again. No doubt many had turned the power of the press to evil and lies—that had been demonstrated over and over in the year past when even the governments of great nations enforced vigorous control of the press or dominated it entirely in order to control the thinking and the conduct of people and armies. But for Christmas John wanted to believe that the good that printing had brought into the world would win—that men would rise to preach with power and others to listen in sincerity—that men would read again the glorious promises of God and their fulfillment in the Christ-child—that love would live again when hate had spent itself and men would build again where lust had destroyed. Then the printed page would be more necessary than ever—then every line would count—then the leaden army that really conquers the world would march boldly forward and occupy once more the great, unconquerable lines of the minds of men and make them strong with truth and warm with love, nurtured on an abiding brotherhood of splendid, undying culture—the sum total of the treasure of the good books and the best articles and the greatest music of all time.

↙   ↙   ↙

The bells of Saint Thomas called for the Children's Vesper and John was glad that he could walk with them into a great church and watch the centuries roll away and the Holy Night return for the nineteen hundred and fortieth time, because God had given men the wisdom to transmit His word through the leaden army marching over the paper highways of language into all the world.

The children were singing as they marched up the crowded aisles—Charles Wesley's hymn—two hundred years old, but new with faith born of the deathless story—

"Mild He lays His glory by,
    Born that man no more may die,
    Born to raise the sons of earth,
    Born to give them second birth.
    Come, Desire of Nations, come,
    Fix in us Thy humble home;
    Oh, to all Thyself impart,
    Formed in each believing heart!
    Hark! the herald angels sing,
    'Glory to the new born King!'"

Opposite page
The Morning Star of Christmas
by Knute Heldner

A Sheaf of Christmas Verse

SELECTED BY G. B. F. HALLOCK

THE ROAD

O wondrous Child of Bethlehem!
  O Man of Majesty!
Who lifted high above the star
  The cross of Calvary!
Christ of the lowly manger,
  Christ of Gethsemane,
Bless any heart this Christmas night
  That takes the road to Thee!

DOROTHY LOUISE THOMAS.

BETHLEHEM

I shall not tarry over scrolls
  That chart the planets of the night;
Nor follow paths of endless goals
  The ordered orbs of Heaven's light;
Nor shall I halt with sense and mind
  At palace, porch, or merchant's mart;
My caravan shall press to find
  A Savior for my hungry heart.

HENRY WEBB FARRINGTON.

THE STAR

O little town, O little town,
  Upon the hills afar,
We see you, like a thing sublime,
  Across the great, grey wastes of time,
And men go up and men go down,
  But follow still the Star.

CLINTON SCOLLARD.

STAR OF MY HEART

Except the Christ be born again tonight
In dreams of all men, saints and sons of shame,
The world will never see His kingdom bright.
Stars of all hearts, lead onward through the night
Past death-black deserts, doubts without a name,
Past hills of pain and mountains of new sin
To that far sky where mystic births begin,
Where dreaming ears the angel-song shall win.
Our Christmas shall be rare at dawning there,
And each shall find his brother fair,
Like a little child within:
All hearts of the earth shall find new birth
And wake no more to sin.

VACHEL LINDSAY.

THERE WAS A JOYOUS HOSTLER

There was a joyous hostler
  Who knelt on Christmas morn
Beside the radiant manger
  Wherein the Lord was born.
His heart was full of laughter,
  His soul was full of bliss,
When Jesus on His mother's lap
  Gave him His hand to kiss.

Unbar your heart this evening
  And keep no stranger out,
Take from your soul's great portal
  The barrier of doubt.
To humble folk and weary
  Give hearty welcoming,
Your breast shall be tomorrow
  The cradle of a King.

JOYCE KILMER.

ADORATION

The Prince of Peace with Power and Might,
Was sent from God, a Holy Light.
The wisemen saw the guiding star,
And travelling followed it afar
To worship God's begotten Son,
The Savior, Master, Holy One.

A Heaven's Light our Father gave,
For Jesus Christ was born to save.
With humble hearts we bend the knee,
In grateful love adoring Thee,
The Christ our King of humble birth,
The gracious Gift of God to earth.

EARNEST LEE WOMACK.

THE KINGS OF THE EAST

The Kings of the East are riding
  Tonight to Bethlehem.
The sunset glows dividing,
The Kings of the East are riding;
A star their journey guiding,
  Gleaming with gold and gem.
The Kings of the East are riding
  Tonight to Bethlehem.

There beams above the manger
  The child-face of a star;
Amid the stars a stranger,
It beams above the manger;
What means this ether-ranger
  To pause where poor folk are?
There beams above a manger
  The child-face of a star.

KATHARINE LEE BATES.

Händel's Messiah

An Immortal Classic in Christmas Music

BY M. BURNETTE THOMPSON

"Majora Canamus"

And without controversy great is the mystery of godliness: God was manifest in the flesh, justified in the Spirit, seen of angels, preached among the Gentiles, believed on in the world, received up into glory.

I TIMOTHY 3:16

In whom are hid all the treasures of wisdom and knowledge.

COLOSSIANS 2:3

THE scriptural passages above appeared in the word-book which was compiled for the first performance of *Messiah* in 1742 at Dublin, Ireland. Strangely enough, it would not be difficult to paraphrase the same verses so that they might testify to the greatness of the oratorio itself and to the genius who composed it. Without controversy, this oratorio towers above all others in universal appeal and affection. Surely God is made manifest in its sublime music which expounds the most important historical facts of the religion of Christ. However carefully one searches among the great musical tone-poets, one fails to find a composer who has "preached among the Gentiles" as extensively with a single composition as has Georg Friedrich Händel.

Undoubtedly Händel experienced a rare religious exaltation during the composing of *Messiah*. For twenty-four days he was completely withdrawn from the things of this world so that he believed he dwelt in the pastures of God. Often as not, the food which his man-servant brought to him was left untouched. When the "Hallelujah Chorus" at the end of Part II was completed, the servant found him at the table, with tears streaming from his eyes. Afterwards Händel explained, "I did think I did see all Heaven before me, and the great God Himself!" There are moments in a few mortals' lives when man catches a glimpse of eternity. Of a certainty, Händel, for a moment of nearly a month, was "received up into glory" and to him were revealed in great measure "the treasures of [musical] wisdom and knowledge."

The lay-musician might be heard defining an oratorio rather vaguely in this fashion: "It is a great work—you know—for chorus, orchestra and big singers, and we hear it at least once a year—generally about Christmas time." A truth it seems that *Messiah* and the term *oratorio* are often used almost synonymously. In England the name Händel is indeed a household word to rich and poor alike, and the greatest of his oratorios, the *Messiah*, has taken a place of devout veneration among the populace. Performances of it have steadily become more frequent during the last hundred years. With many choral societies in England, America, and Germany, it has become an annual musical event at the Christmas season. The very conception of the work itself is one of the sublimest that could engage the attention of the human mind—the great events in the life of the Savior—and it struck down into the depths of Händel's religious nature.

This spiritual profundity is not surprising for the seeds of religious thought were planted and nurtured early in Händel's youth. Although an Englishman by adoption, Georg Friedrich Händel was born of Gottfried and Dorothea Händel in the Saxon town of Halle, Germany. Frau Dorothea devoted her life and energies to the training of her children, whom she educated to a belief in God and the best instincts of the home. Probably due to her strong Lutheran faith, which she carefully passed on to Georg Friedrich, the great influence of religion began to stir in the boy, which later found its true expression in his church music and *Messiah*. The boy's regular visits to the Liebfrauenkirche with his Aunt Anna and later his work there with the organist, Zachau, were impressionable in no small degree. Händel also attended the Lutheran Gymnasium, or Halle Grammar School of which the head was a certain Praetorius, who was a music-loving rector. He had been caught up in the puritanical spirit of pietism which was spreading at Halle, and imparted to the students his belief in the power of music to develop religious thought.

The events which preceded the noontide of Händel's life were a series of fluctuating successes and failures such as are often found in the development of a genius. The few years immediately preceding the creation of *Messiah* were dark with anxieties. Unsuccessful concert seasons had followed one upon another, thereby dragging Händel farther into debt and ultimately into bankruptcy. Rival opera-managers brought in Italian singers and operas which were preferred above those of Händel. Popular taste was also swayed by a new and cheaper brand such as the *Beggar's Opera*. Even the forces of nature seemed pitted against him; an unusually severe winter in London kept many faithful patrons away from the concerts. Added to this was his own poor health and the mental distress he suffered. Shunned on the streets, he seldom appeared there. It was a great satisfaction to his jealous enemies that London was renewing its old belief that Händel was finished.

Then arrived a crisis in the life of the Saxon composer, and with it the event which stands out like a beacon light in musical history. Out of this welter of suffering, Händel created a diversion and that diversion was the glorious *Messiah*. (It is not strictly correct to call it *The Messiah*. Only twice is Händel known to have referred to this work as *The Messiah*.) He could have had no thought of producing it immediately because he put it away in a drawer for seven weeks after its completion. The sickening experiences of the past few years discouraged the mere thought of publication.

Händel had no doubt become intensely stimulated by the words for *Messiah* which he had received from Charles Jennens, also librettist for some previous works. Without these wonderful words, so carefully selected and well arranged, no work could have made the appeal

George Frideric Händel

that this oratorio made. Yet the personality of Charles Jennens was the most unlikely one to be associated with Händel or such a text. No two men could have been more different. Jennens was the descendant of a manufacturing family from whom he had inherited great wealth. A large portion of the fortune was spent on a palatial residence at Gopsall, in Leicestershire, where there hangs today a full-length portrait of Händel by Hudson. His pompousness, conceit, and lavish mode of living earned for him the nickname of the "Gopsall Solyman the Magnificent."

When Jennens took his proofs to his printer in Red Lion Passage, a very short distance from his home, then on Ormond Street, he rode in a magnificent carriage, drawn by horses with plumes, and attended by four lackeys. Upon arrival at the passage, it was the duty of a servant to get down and sweep the pavement free of oyster shells or any other rubbish before his master descended. Yet in spite of such display, Jennens maintained an avid interest in literature and was always beneficent friend to the arts.

Jennens' correspondence reveals that he felt he knew more about the making of an oratorio than did Händel. In one letter he speaks of Mr. Händel's head as being more "full of maggots than ever." After enumerating two reasons for this statement he concludes by saying:

"His third maggot is a Hallelujah which he has trump'd up at the end of his oratorio since I went into the Country, because he thought the conclusion of the oratorio not Grand enough; tho' if that were the case 'twas his own fault, for the words would have bore as Grand Musick as he could have set 'em to: but this Hallelujah, Grand as it is, comes in very nonsensically, having no matter of relation to what goes before. And this is the more extraordinary, because he refused to set a Hallelujah at the end of the first chorus in the oratorio, where I had placed one and where it was to be introduced with the utmost propriety upon a pretense that it would make the entertainment too long. I could tell you more of his maggots; but it grows late and I must defer the rest till I write next, by which time, I doubt not, more new ones will breed in his Brain."

The work referred to in this letter was the oratorio *Saul,* but even on *Messiah* Jennens held his opinions above those of Händel. A letter to a friend reads: "I shall show you a collection I gave Händel, called *Messiah,* which I value highly, and he has made a fine entertainment out of it, though not so good as he might and ought to have done. I have with great difficulty made him correct some of the grossest faults in the composition. But he retained his overture obstinately, in which there are some passages far unworthy of the *Messiah.*" Nevertheless, he must have been a generous soul, for Händel never broke friendship with him, and left him two pictures in his will.

A recent biographer of Händel supplies the information that Jennens never compiled the words of *Messiah.* Newman Flower's investigations reveal that the work was done by a humble little clergyman named Pooley, who lived with Jennens as his secretary. Living almost in the capacity of a slave to Charles Jennens, he was frequently called upon to perform most unpleasant tasks and was drawn into Jennens' literary controversies. That the arrogant master palmed off Pooley's words as his own was not known to Händel at any rate, and the matter may still be one of conjecture. Händel eagerly accepted this libretto and began the work of compo-

sition at the end of August, 1741, in his house on Brook Street. In exactly twenty-four days, the oratorio was done. Indeed, an almost superhuman feat and truly a divinely inspired work.

Some time during that same summer, Händel had received an invitation from the Lord-Lieutenant of Ireland, and the Governors of three Dublin institutions of charity, to give some benefit concerts there. Encouraged by the Irish admiration, Händel accepted the invitation and set out for Dublin by packet-boat on the fourth of November. Contrary winds necessitated a stop-over at the picturesque city of Chester. During the stay, Händel asked Mr. Baker, the town-organist, whether there were any choirmen in the Cathedral who could sing at sight as he wished to try over some pieces of his new oratorio. A printer named Janson was recommended and a meeting took place. But the rehearsal went badly. The impatient Händel became enraged and with a volley of words cried out, "You schountrel! Tit you not tell me dat you could sing at soite?" "Yes, sir," replied the poor fellow, "but not *at first sight.*"

Dublin at this time was a very musical city. A new concert room, capable of accommodating an audience of six hundred persons, had recently been erected by William Neal in Fishamble Street, then a fashionable quarter. The Musical Academy, which performed once a year for charities, held its meetings there. Members of this society and members of the Philharmonic Society augmented by the choirs of both cathedrals in the city were the vocal forces at hand for Händel's great choruses.

Händel opened his concert season two days before Christmas. From beginning to end, it was a series of ovations. It was not until March 23, 1742, that there appeared any mention of *Messiah.* Then an announcement was made in *Faulkner's Journal* that "Mr. Händel's new grand oratorio called *The Messiah,*" was to be given "For Relief of the Prisoners in the Severals Gaols, and for the support of Mercer's Hospital in Stephen's Street, and for the Charitable Infirmary on the Inn's Quay." It was also made known that a ticket for the rehearsal would be given gratis to anyone who bought a ticket for the first performance to be given April 13th. The same journal for April 10th lauded the rehearsal and added a note requesting, "the Favour of the ladies not to come with hoops this day to the Musik Hall in Fishamble Street. The gentlemen are desired to come without their swords." Thus an audience of seven hundred people was accommodated and the three charities received the great sum of four hundred pounds.

Of the singers at this first performance, Mrs. Cibber was the most outstanding. She was best known in London as a tragic actress and had acquired a rather colorful reputation in private life. It may be said here that nearly all the renowned singers of Händel's oratorios had distinguished themselves on the stage. An old album which is now in the British Museum, contains this anecdote: "Mrs. Cibber, in *The Messiah,* in Dublin, executed her air so pathetically, that Dr. Delany, the great friend and companion of Swift, exclaimed, as he sat in the boxes, 'Woman, for this, be all thy sins forgiven.'"

By popular demand, the oratorio was given again in Ireland on the third of June. The weather was extremely warm, a circumstance which led the cautious Händel to announce in the *Journal* that "a Pane of Glass will be removed from the top of each of the Windows." This was Händel's last performance in Dublin.

After an absence of nine months Händel returned to London where *Messiah* did not become immediately successful. It was first performed there on March 23, 1743, at Covent Garden, but it was not advertised or sung under its proper title. Religious prejudices prevailed; people argued that any work about the Omnipotent should never be performed in a playhouse. The clergy called the oratorio a sacrilege and Händel a heretic. So *Messiah* was given the title, *A Sacred Oratorio*. The work was given only three times that season but the king was present at one performance. It was on this occasion the audience was exceedingly affected by the music. When the "Hallelujah Chorus" was being sung, they were so transported that they with the king stood up and remained standing until the chorus ended. From this incident has come the custom of rising during the rendition of this number.

It was not until Händel began his performances in aid of the Foundling Hospital that *Messiah* fully came into its own. The hospital had been established in 1741 by a kind-hearted old mariner, Captain Coram, from profits of a trading vessel of which he was master. It was designated as a "Hospital for the Maintenance and Education of Exposed and Deserted Young Children in Lamb's Conduit Fields." The institution was a continual source of pleasure to Händel in his late years.

The concerts in the hospital's chapel proved so popular that Händel gave the institution a copy of the *Messiah* score, and promised to conduct it every year for the benefit of charity. The administrators of the hospital sought to put the composer's intentions into some legal form and prepared a petition to parliament which read thus: "That in order to raise a further sum for the benefit of the said charity, Georg Friedrich Händel, Esq., hath been charitably pleased to give to this corporation a composition of music, called 'the Oratorio of *The Messiah*,' composed by him; the said Georg Friedrich Händel reserving to himself only the liberty of performing the same for his own benefit during his life: And whereas, the said benefaction can not be secured to the sole use of your petitioners, therefore humbly pray that leave may be given to bring in a bill for the purposes aforesaid." When one of the committee presented this petition to Händel for his approval, the lat-

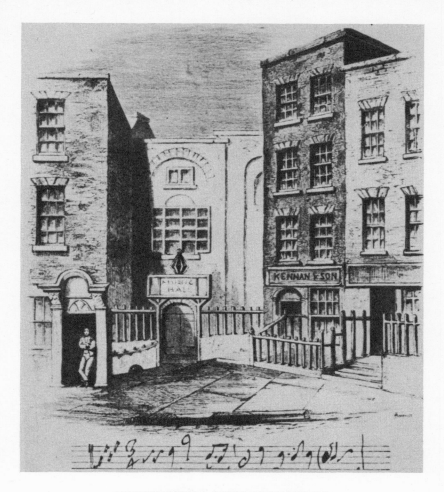

NEAL'S MUSIC HALL IN DUBLIN
Whereat *Messiah* Was First Performed

ter burst into one of his characteristic rages, protesting vehemently that he would not allow his music to "go to the Parliament."

The hospital honored Händel for his generosity by making him one of its governors. Shortly before that offer, Händel had presented the Hospital with a fine organ which he opened in person on the first of May, 1750, with a performance of *Messiah*. All the tickets were sold out days before at Batson's Coffee House and White's Chocolate House. The chapel could accommodate a thousand persons but more than that number were turned away at the doors. Therefore Händel repeated the concert a fortnight later for the benefit of those turned away.

No less than eleven performances were given in the chapel between 1750 and 1759 with benefits amounting to nearly seven thousand pounds. The sum was greatly increased after Händel's death. Perhaps no single work has accomplished as much for charity as has the *Messiah* throughout the years. Literally, "it has fed the hungry, clothed the naked, fostered the orphan and comforted the sorrowing."

In his will, Händel bequeathed the hospital "A fair copy of the score and all the parts of my Oratorio called the *Messiah*." The score which is in the handwriting of his amanuensis, Christopher Smith, has been carefully preserved. The parts were completely overlooked until 1894 when an organist, Mr. Walton, discovered them in an old cupboard near the organ. Another copy of *Messiah* which was among the music manuscripts bequeathed to Händel's faithful pupil and secretary, Christopher Smith, is now at Buckingham Palace. It is recounted that Mr. Smith once refused an offer of two thousand pounds made by the King of Prussia for the *Messiah* manuscript. He would neither part with it nor allow it to go out of the country after his death.

The *Messiah* was performed thirty-four times during Händel's life with the composer himself conducting all the performances. Conducting with the baton was not practiced at this time. The "conductor" sat at the harpsichord or organ playing the *continuo* or figured bass, and directed as best he could with the assistance of the first violinist, who beat time with his bow whenever he could. Playing the *continuo* was a very skilled art of which Händel was a great master. Even when his sight was far gone, he gave two performances of *Messiah* "with an extempore on the organ." His sight was too dimmed to allow his playing from notes. For the last seven or eight years of his life, he was virtually blind. An operation was performed to relieve the condition, but it was unsuccessful.

It was at an April performance of the *Messiah* at Covent Garden that the blind master collapsed after the glorious "*Amen* Chorus." He was hurried to his home and put to bed from which he was never to rise again. It now being already Easter week, Händel prayed that he might breathe his last on Good Friday, "in hope of meeting his good God, his sweet Lord and Savior on the day of His resurrection." Strangely enough, the wish was granted. On Good Friday, April 13, 1759, Händel passed away at the age of seventy-four years. The English nation gave him its highest honor—burial in Poets' Corner in Westminster Abbey. Over three thousand people gathered in the Abbey to see Händel buried. An English newspaper carried this brief but dignified account of the rites:

> "Last night about Eight o'clock, the remains of the late great Mr. Händel were deposited at the foot of the Duke of Argyll's Monument in Westminster Abbey; and though he had mention'd being privately interr'd, yet from the Respect due to so celebrated a Man, the Bishop, Prebends, and the whole choir attended to pay the last Honours due to his memory; the Bishop himself performed the Service. A monument is also to be erected for him, which there is no doubt but his Works will even outlive. There was almost the greatest Concourse of People of all Ranks ever seen upon such or indeed upon any other Occasion."

Four years later the monument by Roubiliac was dedicated. By an extraordinary coincidence this monument was Roubiliac's last important work while his statue of Händel at Vauxhall had been his first. It represents Händel leaning over a table covered with musical instruments. An organ occupies the entire background and above Händel's head an angel seated on a cloud, and playing upon a harp, seems to be dictating to him. Beneath Händel's hand holding a pen, is laid the *Messiah* open at the thrilling words, "I know that my Redeemer liveth."

All England again paid tribute to Händel in an elaborate manner at the Westminster Abbey in 1784. The occasion was the Händel Commemoration in which five days were occupied with the performance of Händel's music alone. The *Messiah* was a feature of the celebration and was performed with an orchestra of two hundred and forty-nine musicians and two hundred and seventy-five voices. The oratorio was given annually on Christmas Eve from 1791-1811. Again on the centenary of his death, there was a performance at the Crystal Palace with an orchestra of four hundred and sixty pieces and a choir of two thousand and seven hundred persons blended in triumphant voice.

And now in countless hamlets or cities in England, America, Germany, and other countries, choruses unite and begin their rehearsals for a performance of parts of the *Messiah,* usually before the Christmas season. Each community builds its own traditions which are the strongest forces in perpetuating culture. From the north of England, a Dr. Coward of Sheffield wrote the *Musical Times* of this custom:

"Both at Huddersfield and Sheffield we all sing 'Christians, Awake' before the *Messiah,* if the oratorio is performed within a few days of Christmas Day, and the singing of the hymn is such a heart-warming thing that not a few go to the performance just for the joy of it. Somehow after a good sing of 'Christians, Awake' one feels 'Christmassy.' "

The Händel and Haydn Society in Boston alone has given *Messiah* more than a hundred times since 1818. Most conspicuous in American musical traditions today is the annual production of the oratorio at Easter by the midwestern town of Lindsborg, Kansas. Farmers, business men, housewives, and college students gather faithfully for rehearsals, irrespective of age, occupation, or distance. Guest soloists are imported, but the orchestra is comprised of students from Bethany College, a small Swedish Lutheran institution, immensely proud of its musical tradition.

The great choruses and arias have become so familiar to the public that it appears superfluous to interpret the music itself. Furthermore, it would be futile to attempt a description. The music, as must any great work, speaks for itself. Regarding the plan of the oratorio, it suffices to say that in the first part, the coming of the Savior of mankind is treated. The second part, in which the life, sufferings, and resurrection of the Lord are treated, is the most impressive portion. Here is experienced the majestic and solemn chorus, "Behold the Lamb of God." The aria for alto, "He Was Despised," is one of the most deeply expressive songs that has ever been written depicting sorrow.

The orchestral interlude, which depicts the vigil of the shepherds, is the tone picture, "The Pastoral Symphony"—simple as a psalm tune but yet truly sublime. It has often been said that this movement is founded on an old Calabrian melody which Händel heard at Christmas when he was at Rome in 1709. Here he heard the Calabrian Pifferari (players of the fife) who came every year to Rome to celebrate the birth of Christ by singing and playing an ancient melody in memory of the shepherds of Bethlehem. The old monarch, George the Third, king of England, once described his reaction to this number with this remark, "When I hear it I seem to see the stars shining!"

The oratorio could have closed at this point but Händel carried it to a third part which is devoted to the "things hereafter"— death, resurrection, and life eternal. It forms, as it were, a credo, opening with the confession of faith, "I Know That My Redeemer Liveth," and closing with the exultant "Amen" fugue, overpowering in its majestic sweep, overwhelming in its triumph.

Speaking of the impression that this eternally beautiful masterpiece has always produced, the words of the actress, Mrs. Abingdon, are recalled: "Oh, I can only think of Händel as a builder of cathedrals . . . glorious within and without, massive in structure, and here and there a spire tapering up to heaven itself, and yet with countless columns made beautiful with the finest carving."

The source is unknown but some commentator has remarked that truly the great tone-cathedral of Händel's *Messiah* is an erection of which all nations of the world may be proud, and for which humanity must be ever grateful. This superb masterpiece of tonal art may well be considered a foretaste of the music that will delight and exalt the human soul in a future, more blessed, state of existence.

Uncle Heinrich the Woodcarver

Illustrated by Regina Koelnau

The great autobahn roads which interlink the parts of
New Germany cut the corners of the Bavarian Alps, but
they despair of ever thrusting their ugly strips of pavement into the heart of them. Those jagged peaks have a
lofty indifference for the visions of empire building
dictators. Armored trucks roar by on these military
highways, but the crags hurl back the engine roars in

scorn. Only faint echoes of the outside world penetrate
inward; and they, in turn, make no ripple in the surface
of daily living in the little villages which thrive on the
mountains' roots. Unruffled as the quiet Alpine lakes are
the sturdy folk who live within. True, their young sons
are in uniform, but when in history have their young
sons not been in uniform? Wars and political intrigues

are not drama in Bavaria, but births, deaths, marriages, and festivals—these are drama the simple peasant folk can understand.

Traumdorf on the Hintersee. Cobblestones and long-eaved houses. Houses with richly carved gables. Houses with roofs shingled in larch and held in place by heavy stones. Houses as gay and inviting in color as was the witch's to Hansel and Gretel, only these are not of chocolate and gingerbread. Houses with heavy oak beams and the plaster rectangles between them frescoed brightly with Biblical characters looking for all the world like jolly, plump Germans. Red geraniums in every window. Little shops with great sausages hung in ropes and festoons from the ceiling. Inns from whose gayly papered interior come merry tinkling airs. Brawny men and women on the streets in richly dyed costumes. Smooth, round-faced young girls with braided hanks of long blonde hair falling over their shoulders. Tassels on the long white woolen stockings of the men. Spangles and embroidered roses on the bodices of the women. Little girls in bright aprons. Lads with colored feathers in their jaunty hats. This was Traumdorf on the Hintersee one hundred years ago. This is Traumdorf today.

Behind the village lay the forest, so close that one could stand in the public square on summer evenings and hear the nightingales. It was deep and dark, with only here and there a little opening for a tiny farm or chalet. In the summer peasants on the mountain side rumbled to and from the village on a road winding in and out among the trees, but in the winter they used the ski road, dropping dizzily down to the Hintersee. Like mountain eagles they swooped down from the heights, stopped dexterously beside the last house on the village edge, waved cheerily to the faces pressed against the windows, and went into the market square to buy their supplies.

Konrad and Anna peered anxiously out of the shuttered windows of the little house at the end of the ski-road. Konrad stuck his tongue on the frosted pane to make his peephole larger.

"Mutter," he called, "do you think Uncle Heinrich will come?"

Mutter had answered the question a hundred times in the last two hours, but her voice from the kitchen was kind.

"Uncle Heinrich always comes for Christmas, Mäuschen mein."

"But it will be dark, and we cannot go to put a tree on Groszmutter's grave."

"Ach."

Groszvater rapped his cane on the floor. He was not so patient as Mutter, and when it came to doubting his oldest son's filial loyalty he must take his long pipe from his mouth and protest.

"There he is! There he is!" screamed Anna, who was more vigilant at her peephole than Konrad.

Sure enough, far up the mountain side was a dark speck against the snow—a hurtling speck which grew and grew, and in no time was Uncle Heinrich himself, with a long red feather in his cap, a bulging knapsack on his back, and two small evergreens strapped on his shoulders. Right up to the front door he sped and stopped squarely before the shrine of Mary and the Baby Jesus. It was as big as Mutter, and Uncle Heinrich himself had carved and placed it in the niche. Tonight they would light the lamp there, for it was Heiliger Abend.

Uncle Heinrich knocked the snow off his skis, set them against the wall, and swept the two children in the doorway into his arms. He kissed Anna's apple cheeks and rubbed Konrad's face with his prickly whiskers until he squealed. He kissed Mutter, too, and shook hands with Groszvater, who hobbled from his great chair to greet him.

Mutter helped Uncle Heinrich take the knapsack off his back. Konrad and Anna looked shyly at it, knowing that it was full of secrets. Heinrich did not come down to the village with everyone else on Copper and Silver Sunday, when the shops were open for Christmas customers. Not even on the last Sunday before Christmas—Golden Sunday to the shopkeepers—did he mix with the trinket-buying crowds. Uncle Heinrich made his own Christmas presents in his little house high on the mountain. Nor did that mean his gifts were crude and poor, for even the shops in München sold things he made with his magic knife.

But there was no time to speculate on what was in the knapsack this year, for Mutter had thrown her bright shawl over her head and was ready to go to the churchyard. Konrad and Anna put extra socks on their feet and bundled into their coats. They trotted in front of Mutter and Uncle, drinking in the excitement of the village street. They saw servant maids flitting by the great windows of the Bürgermeister's house, scampering hither and thither in their gay gowns of multi-colored plaid, small caps, and spangled blouses. The forest of Christmas trees around the fountain had thinned out in the last day, but even yet late buyers scurried to get theirs before the four o'clock church bell rang and all business ceased. People still crowded into the stores and milled around the outdoor booths travelling peddlers had set up. In but one hour all this would be changed.

The streets and all public places would be empty of people, save for a straggler or two hurrying home to the family hearth. The shop windows with their bold notices of "Weihnachts Geschenke" in fancy letters and their holly and icicle ornaments would stare out on silent streets.

Konrad held the churchyard gate open for the others. There had been many before them, and the cemetery was a bright miniature forest with miniature trees. They all knelt around Groszmutter's grave while Uncle Heinrich planted a tree in the snow. But they did not follow Uncle when he planted the other tree in a far corner. When he came back, there was a tear trembling in the furrow of his cheek, and they knew he was remembering the Mädchen who had died long ago. That was why Uncle Heinrich had no children, Mutter had told them.

The red Gepäckwagen was pulling away from the house when they drew near home again. Konrad and Anna dashed at the big package on the step, but Mutter, with surprisingly nimble feet, was there before them.

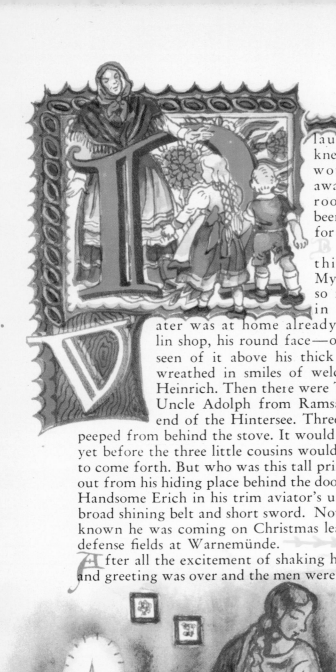

"Nein, nein!" she laughed, and they knew that this, too, would be popped away in the front room, which had been locked to them for two weeks now.

But who could think long of the Mystery Room with so many surprises in the kitchen? Vater was at home already from the violin shop, his round face—or what could be seen of it above his thick mustaches—all wreathed in smiles of welcome for Uncle Heinrich. Then there were Tante Marie and Uncle Adolph from Ramsau on the other end of the Hintersee. Three little towheads peeped from behind the stove. It would be several hours yet before the three little cousins would be bold enough to come forth. But who was this tall prince who stepped out from his hiding place behind the door? Uncle Erich! Handsome Erich in his trim aviator's uniform with the broad shining belt and short sword. Not even Vater had known he was coming on Christmas leave from the air defense fields at Warnemünde.

After all the excitement of shaking hands and kissing and greeting was over and the men were quietly smoking their long pipes in the next room, Konrad and Anna tried politely to interest the little cousins in drawing pictures on the misted windows in the kitchen, but they could only tag Tante Marie and hide their faces in her heavy red skirt. She shook them off impatiently, for she and Mutter were bustling about with supper, but they substituted their fists in their eyes for her skirts and would not look at Konrad and Anna. Finally in high scorn the two left them to the women and went in to the men. Here curling clouds of smoke almost obscured the ceiling as one or another pair of cheeks poured forth a dark stream. Konrad climbed into Uncle Heinrich's lap and played with the squirrel's tail dangling from his pipe. Anna, of course, twined her arms about Erich's neck. Konrad looked at her fondling Erich's sword hilt and tracing her fingers over the eagle's wings on his breast. Silly girl! Did she think flying aeroplanes was better than carving things out of wood? Could Erich make deer who looked at you over their shoulders and almost talked? Could he make saucy little rabbits and impudent squirrels? Could he turn a stick of wood into the tender Christ Child? Konrad drew Uncle Heinrich's head down to his lips.

"Uncle," he whispered, "will you teach me to be a wood carver like you?"

"Ja wohl, little squirrel!" he whispered so hard in Konrad's ear that it tickled.

Satisfied that Uncle Heinrich knew that *he*, at least, was not beguiled by a fine uniform, Konrad snuggled deeper in the warm arms. It may have been the smoke in his eyes—anyway, the next thing he knew Uncle Heinrich was shaking him and there was a great scurrying about and moving of chairs and

benches to the long table. Such a large family they were! Twelve in all from Groszvater to the little cousin, who had to have a footstool on her chair in order to reach her plate. Heiliger Abend meal was not big—not so big as to-morrow's dinner would be. But there was plenty of cold meat, ham, and sausage, with cheese and pumpernickel. And—wunderbar!—there was coffee! Vater's mustaches actually twitched with excitement when Mutter brought in the big steaming pot. There wasn't any coffee to be had in the stores this year, but wise Mütterchen had saved some on the topmost shelf in the cupboard. Uncle Adolph nearly cried with joy into his mug, for Tante Marie hadn't had a grain of coffee in the house for two years. They had to drink parched barley coffee even on Christmas.

After supper there was more smoking while the women washed the dishes. But no drooping eyes for the little ones *now*. The three little cousins had forgotten their shyness in their growing excitement and whispered with Konrad and Anna in the corner.

"Little spies!" Vater laughed at them, as he darted out of the Mystery Room to consult with Mutter.

"Come, Kinder," Erich called from where he sat talking with Uncle Heinrich, "would you like to hear about the Christmas tree in the barracks?"

But what was that to all the mysterious goings-on in the front room and the sly looks and whispers which passed between the older ones?

The huge, ancient Nürnberg clock hammered off the strokes of eight. No sooner had the last bong died away when a drum was thumped out in the kitchen, and in marched Vater, Konrad's toy drum fastened around his thick middle. Thump! Thump! Everyone burst into laughter and rushed to get in line behind Vater. Thumpety thump! All through the house they marched—up-stairs, downstairs, bedroom, garret, cellar, and all. Thumpety, thumpety, thump, thump! Surely no witch or elf or evil spirit would dare stay indoors with such a noise! The procession halted before the door to the Mystery Room. Vater threw open the door with a great flourish and stepped aside for the rush.

The tree! The tree! There it stood, lighting up the room with its hundred or more candles. Was any tree ever so gaily dressed? Tinsel, wax angels, glistening balls, glass icicles, frost-covered acorns, toys, grapes, golden apples, little dolls, candy sticks, paper chains, *everything!*

The three little cousins were so entranced they could not even squeal. In fact, no one could say a word until the older ones gathered them into a circle and began marching about the tree and singing.

"O Tannenbaum, O Tannenbaum.
Wie grün sind deine Blätter!"
Du grünst nicht nur zur Sommerzeit,
Nein, auch im Winter, wenn es schneit.
O Tannenbaum, O Tannenbaum,
Wie grün sind deine Blätter.

Then they marched the other way and sang, "Stille Nacht, heilige Nacht!"

One of the twigs caught fire. Uncle Heinrich stretched a long arm and crunched it out in his hand, and a delicious, indescribable Tannenduft filled the air. Konrad's wildly beating heart became calm. Unknown to him, the other voices grew softer, as if they would have his clear, sweet treble lead them. Uncle Heinrich's eyes rested tenderly on the small boy's shining face.

 Es ist ein' Ros' entsprungen
Aus einer Wurzel zart,
Als uns die Alten sungen
Aus Jesse kam die Art;
Und hat ein Blümlein bracht,
Mitten im kalten Winter
Wohl zu der halben Nacht.

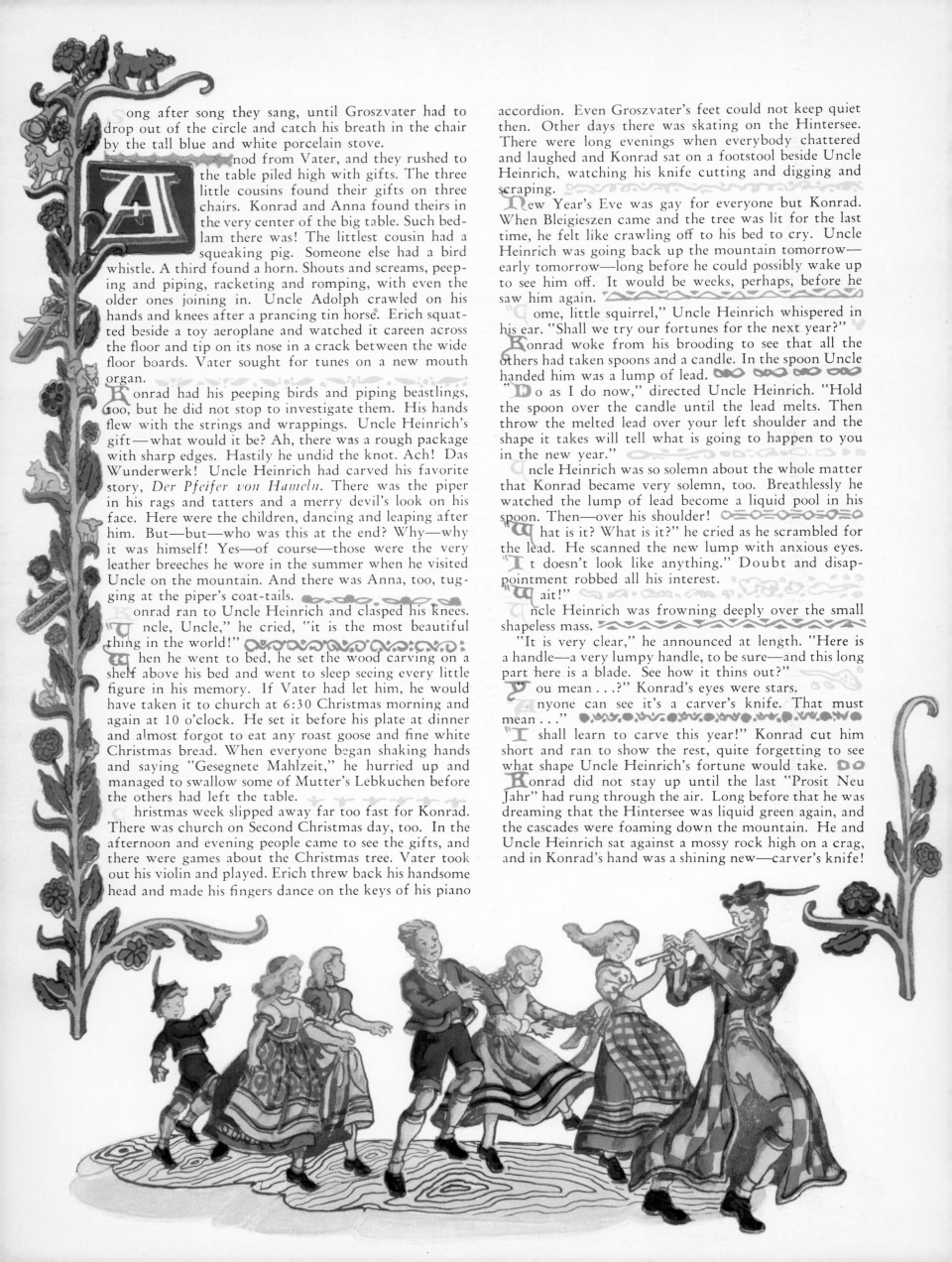

Song after song they sang, until Groszvater had to drop out of the circle and catch his breath in the chair by the tall blue and white porcelain stove.

A nod from Vater, and they rushed to the table piled high with gifts. The three little cousins found their gifts on three chairs. Konrad and Anna found theirs in the very center of the big table. Such bedlam there was! The littlest cousin had a squeaking pig. Someone else had a bird whistle. A third found a horn. Shouts and screams, peeping and piping, racketing and romping, with even the older ones joining in. Uncle Adolph crawled on his hands and knees after a prancing tin horse. Erich squatted beside a toy aeroplane and watched it career across the floor and tip on its nose in a crack between the wide floor boards. Vater sought for tunes on a new mouth organ.

Konrad had his peeping birds and piping beastlings, too, but he did not stop to investigate them. His hands flew with the strings and wrappings. Uncle Heinrich's gift—what would it be? Ah, there was a rough package with sharp edges. Hastily he undid the knot. Ach! Das Wunderwerk! Uncle Heinrich had carved his favorite story, *Der Pfeifer von Hameln*. There was the piper in his rags and tatters and a merry devil's look on his face. Here were the children, dancing and leaping after him. But—but—who was this at the end? Why—why it was himself! Yes—of course—those were the very leather breeches he wore in the summer when he visited Uncle on the mountain. And there was Anna, too, tugging at the piper's coat-tails.

Konrad ran to Uncle Heinrich and clasped his knees. "Uncle, Uncle," he cried, "it is the most beautiful thing in the world!"

When he went to bed, he set the wood carving on a shelf above his bed and went to sleep seeing every little figure in his memory. If Vater had let him, he would have taken it to church at 6:30 Christmas morning and again at 10 o'clock. He set it before his plate at dinner and almost forgot to eat any roast goose and fine white Christmas bread. When everyone began shaking hands and saying "Gesegnete Mahlzeit," he hurried up and managed to swallow some of Mutter's Lebkuchen before the others had left the table.

Christmas week slipped away far too fast for Konrad. There was church on Second Christmas day, too. In the afternoon and evening people came to see the gifts, and there were games about the Christmas tree. Vater took out his violin and played. Erich threw back his handsome head and made his fingers dance on the keys of his piano

accordion. Even Groszvater's feet could not keep quiet then. Other days there was skating on the Hintersee. There were long evenings when everybody chattered and laughed and Konrad sat on a footstool beside Uncle Heinrich, watching his knife cutting and digging and scraping.

New Year's Eve was gay for everyone but Konrad. When Bleigieszen came and the tree was lit for the last time, he felt like crawling off to his bed to cry. Uncle Heinrich was going back up the mountain tomorrow—early tomorrow—long before he could possibly wake up to see him off. It would be weeks, perhaps, before he saw him again.

"Come, little squirrel," Uncle Heinrich whispered in his ear. "Shall we try our fortunes for the next year?"

Konrad woke from his brooding to see that all the others had taken spoons and a candle. In the spoon Uncle handed him was a lump of lead.

"Do as I do now," directed Uncle Heinrich. "Hold the spoon over the candle until the lead melts. Then throw the melted lead over your left shoulder and the shape it takes will tell what is going to happen to you in the new year."

Uncle Heinrich was so solemn about the whole matter that Konrad became very solemn, too. Breathlessly he watched the lump of lead become a liquid pool in his spoon. Then—over his shoulder!

"What is it? What is it?" he cried as he scrambled for the lead. He scanned the new lump with anxious eyes. "It doesn't look like anything." Doubt and disappointment robbed all his interest.

"Wait!"

Uncle Heinrich was frowning deeply over the small shapeless mass.

"It is very clear," he announced at length. "Here is a handle—a very lumpy handle, to be sure—and this long part here is a blade. See how it thins out?"

"You mean . . . ?" Konrad's eyes were stars.

"Anyone can see it's a carver's knife. That must mean . . ."

"I shall learn to carve this year!" Konrad cut him short and ran to show the rest, quite forgetting to see what shape Uncle Heinrich's fortune would take.

Konrad did not stay up until the last "Prosit Neu Jahr" had rung through the air. Long before that he was dreaming that the Hintersee was liquid green again, and the cascades were foaming down the mountain. He and Uncle Heinrich sat against a mossy rock high on a crag, and in Konrad's hand was a shining new—carver's knife!

59

THE ALPS

© Philip D. Gendreau

SWITZERLAND

© Meerkamper from Monkmeyer

61

DAVOS, SWITZERLAND

ENGLAND

© Wide World

SCOTLAND 62

© Keystone View

FINLAND

NORWAY

SWEDEN

NORDIC PINES 66

Christmas Poetry

SONG FOR CHRISTMAS

Sing a song for Christmas,
Of silver-crusted snow,
Of bells that chime in hill and dale,
Of lights that twinkle so.

Sing a song for Christmas,
Of childlike ecstasy,
Of lovely fir trees gaily trimmed,
Of Yuletide melody.

Sing a song for Christmas,
Of sparkling stars above,
Of "Peace on Earth, good-will to men,"
Of God's eternal love.

Sing a song for Christmas,
Of precious Baby King,
Of how He came that we might live,
Sing, weary world—oh, sing!

KAREN ELBA.

THE STAR OF BETHLEHEM

The brightest gleam that ever shone
    Across the dark world's night
Was not reflected from the throne
    Of selfishness or might.
Nor was the torch that led the way
    To any diadem.
It was love's gentle, golden ray—
    The star of Bethlehem.

The light that longest shall abide
    Among the distant years,
And leave on weary faces dried
    The most of human tears,
Is not the glow reflected far
    From splendor's gleaming gem.
It is the light of one lone star—
    The star of Bethlehem.

CLARENCE E. FLYNN.

JUDEAN STAR

This Christmas night is silver-starred on blue;
The spell that touched Judea might be ours
This year, if troubled, clamoring men but knew
The source of power, beyond their greed for powers.
If, seeking stars, we read the Star aright,
Confusion could be silenced with a phrase.
If, unillumined, we perceived the Light,
We should not walk in darkness all our days.
These dull eyes have been blind to glory, long;
Forgive us, Star we did not want to see!
These ears were sealed against the angel song,
Lest it rebuke our old disharmony.
Judea, we would find the Star again,
And hear your "Peace on earth, good-will to men."

ELINOR LENNEN.

CHRISTMAS EVE

How very still it is tonight,
    In city and in town,
The little houses nestle close
    Like babes, 'neath quilts of down.

The sky has sent an ermine wrap
    For Mother Earth to wear,
And placed a crown of diamond stars
    Upon her lovely hair.

All mankind waits the clarion call
    Across the frosty night,
Even winds in leafless trees
    Have stopped their hurried flight.

One breathless moment, then the song
    The Herald Angels sing—
Bells rejoice and Earth goes out
    To meet her glorious King!

KAREN ELBA.

BETHLEHEM INNKEEPER

The inn was full. There was no room.
    And yet, of course, I might have made
Arrangement. But the evening gloom
    Came on—a man must keep his trade—
    The guests were in—they all had paid.

There was no room. The inn was full,
    And it had been a busy day;
So many vexing questions pull
    A landlord's heart. All cannot stay—
    The late ones must be turned away.

The inn was full. There was no room,
    But certainly I could have done
Something if I had known for whom—
    Ah, that my door should be the one
    To shut out Mary and her Son!

B. Y. WILLIAMS.

CAROL AT MIDNIGHT

I stand beneath a blue-black velvet sky,
While, all around me, snowflakes hurry by;
The winds' contralto voices softly sing
To naked trees about a little King.

Long ebon fingers soon begin to play
On wind harps, hung in silver branches gay,
That seem to catch the echo of a cry,
In soft accompaniment to a lullabye.

As midnight bells ring through the frosty night,
The great crescendo reaches heavenly height;
As angels bear the song on golden horn,
Their hurried wings tell me, "The Christ is born!"

KAREN ELBA.

67

For the Children from Possum Run

BY GRACE NOLL CROWELL

Illustration by Knute Heldner

THIS December day the big house with its shutters closed behind its great white pillared porticoes, looked for all the world like a huge sleeping giant. The magnolia trees on the lawn seemed to wrap it about with warm protectiveness, and the winter grass, lovingly tended by black hands, was a dazzling emerald, rich enough and big enough to blanket even the big house.

The front of the building was indeed silent and deserted, but in the back, the yard was electric with shock and excitement. Something was going to happen. Something wonderful!

Mose, the yard man, fairly clapped his heels in his going about. Old Ivory, his huge black wife, the cook for many years at the big house, was all ashake, and bitingly arrogant in her demands on Lilybelle, her son's erstwhile wife, and the mother of little bullet-headed Tobe. The son, Morgan Lindsey, named after Colonel Morgan Lindsey, owner of the big house and proprietor of the great plantation that stretched far away in the distance, had proved a disgrace to the name; but many a rascally namesake has managed to live in the shadow of glory and greatness, and remain unnoticed and unsung, and for the most part, unjailed, as had old Mose's boy.

"Yo' crack yo' heels, Lilybelle," Ivory flung out.

"Get into that house an' give them beds a good airin', an' don't yo' dast look into things yo' no business lookin' into. Yo' har? Now git."

"Morgan Lindsey, ain't yo' wrung them chickens' necks yet? Reckon yo' so lazy even them spindly fryers is too big a job fo' yo'. Get goin', I tell yo'," and, "Mose, Mose," she shrieked, "yo' polish that silvah, an' don't leave no black—har me?" Turning to the turnip greens she was cleaning at the out-of-door trough, she addressed herself to them: "Yo' better git clean. Colonel Lindsey he like his pot licker ungritted same as the next un." Then strangely sweet after her tirade, her reedy voice lifted in song:

> "Yo' said if I be lifted up
> I'll be yo' fathah, I'll be yo' mothah,
> I'll be yo' sistah, I'll be yo' brothah,
> An' I'se gwine to lift yo' up."

Colonel J. Morgan Lindsey and his wife, "Miss Caroline," were coming home. For a year they had been gone from the big house: a strange, terrible, feverish year. They had been running away from a great overwhelming sorrow, and they found that it could not be done. Last year their little daughter, Caroline, had died as suddenly as a candle flame that is blown out by a quick strong wind. Their little lovely, eager-hearted, eight-year-old Caroline, the only child, the only child they could ever have, had been there one moment, and gone the next! Little Caroline who loved surprises; who could scarcely wait for any happy coming event, had gone in a breath, leaving unopened the gayly wrapped, mysterious packages labeled for her and grouped at the foot of the great shining tree that Christmas morning. She had left the big house that her presence had lighted like southern sunshine; had left the great halls and rooms as empty as if there were no life left anywhere at all, and the father and mother, stricken wordless with sorrow, and numbed with shock, knowing that it was God who had called their child into heaven and had closed the door, tried hard to be reconciled, to bear their sorrow as they should, knowing that all His ways are right and good. Yet in their wild grieving they turned to each other and said:

"We must get away—away from the emptiness of the house, the rooms. We must! We must! We will travel far. We will fly on great planes. Perhaps the wind from the stars will blow the agony from our hearts. We will sail on great liners. It may be the waves will soothe us and give us rest and peace. We will not come back until —until we are able to bear the house, the rooms, to bear Christmas here. . . ."

There is nothing more heartening to a weary southern traveler than the welcome home of long time faithful and trusted colored servants. Miss Caroline, dreading, in spite of her high resolve, to enter the house of tragic memories, fearful lest her new-found courage fail her, felt that warmth envelop her, and was humbly grateful for it. There was old Ivory, her arms widely outstretched, reaching out—not quite touching her— embracing her, as it were, in her own and only way. Her "Lor' Mis' Ca'oline, yo' sho does look good to me! An' I'se sho glad to see yo', too, Boss-Man!"; Lilybelle's simpering and Morgan Lindsey's stammering; even little bullet-headed Tobe's white-toothed grin from behind his mother's skirts, were joyously welcoming.

"We decided to come home for Christmas, Ivory. We are going to open the house. We shall have a Christmas tree," Miss Caroline said bravely. "We felt that it would be better so."

"Sho enough, Mis' Ca'oline? Is yo' sho yo' kin do it?" Ivory's rolling eyes showed her astonishment. "Is yo' sho?"

"Yes, Ivory, we are quite sure. Little Caroline came to me in a dream. She was beautiful—like golden light. She was like all the joy there is in the world. She spoke to me. She told me she is happy, that she wants us to be happy. She wanted us to come home, and so we came." Ivory's eyes all but rolled from her head at this. A "hant," no matter how greatly beloved the departed one might be, was too unearthly, too terrifying for her nerves, deeply embedded though they were.

"And so we came home for Christmas. We are going to open the house. We shall have a tree," Miss Caroline continued. "We felt we should. That it would be best."

"Yo' all will ask all the city folks, ah reckon?"

"No, Ivory. We aren't going to invite our old friends this time. We shall begin very special preparations tomorrow. We want all the children from Possum Run to come to our Christmas party. Every one of them."

"Yo' doesn't mean it, Mis' Ca'oline, does yo'? Why, they'se jest pore white trash. Yo' all mean the Hill chilluns, isn't yo'? They'se Grade A. They'se really Grade A." Ivory had bottled too much milk to fail to know the significance of the letter.

"No, Ivory, we feel that little Caroline would like for us to go into the highways and the byways this time. Oh, Ivory, she is so beautifully, goldenly happy! She wants everyone to be happy. She said so. She spoke of other children. . . ." And Miss Caroline closed her eyes a moment to recall more clearly the radiant vision. "She would like for us to do this thing we have planned. I know she would."

"Aw right, Mis' Ca'oline," Ivory hastened, wide eyed and shivery at the thought of the heavenly apparition. "Mose'll go down tomorrow an' invite 'em. But I spect we won't git cleaned up all wintah once they been heah. They'se Grade B folks, an' mighty pore Grade B." And thus having unburdened herself she waddled kitchenward, singing at the top of her voice:

> "Yes, the blessed Christ was bo'n,
> In a meek an' 'umble fo'm,
> To reach a wretched sinnah just like me,
> Had he come a hia'h way
> Then the rich would have their say,
> He's the joy o' my salvation, yes he is,
> Yes he is."

Early the next morning the great preparations began. Five days in which to accomplish the innumerable, all but impossible, tasks: the great tree to be cut in the woods and brought home to be decorated more brilliantly, more beautifully than any tree had ever been; the many gifts to be bought; cooking to be done until the huge kitchen range would glow and dance to keep up with it all; Ivory's black arms white to the elbows in flour; Mose, flapping about his tasks for all the world like the turkeys whose heads he would cut off.

Morgan Lindsey, driving the great limousine to the near-by city, parking in front of dime stores, or driving through the throngs while Miss Caroline shopped in the big stores. Little Tobe at his side, his eyes popping at the unusual sights, missed nothing of the city's gay excitement. He saw the Salvation Army lassies clanging their bells above the screened kettles that held the bright tossed coins. He blinked at the city workers as they climbed the poles of the street lamps to finish their task of hanging the fragrant cedar wreaths, and the red and silver bells there for decoration. He even thought—yes, he did glimpse a red robed figure—the huge bearded Santa Claus who roamed the streets ready and willing to lend a heavily swathed ear to little children's wants. This, indeed, was wonderland to little bullet-headed Tobe from the country. And there was Miss Caroline, coming home from her great tasks, tired enough to rest, to sleep the night through, a thing she had not been able to do through the past long year. Always she was sustained by the glory of what she had seen: little Caroline, glad and happy in her heavenly home, with Christmas more dazzlingly beautiful there than any on earth could be. Little Caroline, wanting her father and mother to be happy; wanting them to forget a thing that was past; that no longer mattered because of the present radiance and the joys that are waiting in the eternal Christmases.

Mose had done his work with reluctance, but he had done it well. "Who was he to be associating with white trash?" he thought as he trudged from weathered shack to tumble-down shack in "Possum Run." "How many chilluns yo' all got?" he would question disdainfully. "My Boss-Man say he wants fo' yo' all to let yo' young-uns come to a pahty at the big house, six o'clock Christmas Eve. He sho does." Then on and on: "How many yo' all got? Five? An' yo'? An' yo'?" magically storing the number away under his gray thatch of wool to be remembered later. And on he went, receiving stoical replies and laconic promises that all the children would come trudging across the fields to the big house on Christmas Eve. And they came. How they did come! Emmie Porgy, her tattered rags pinned together; Johnnie Cook, barefoot and unwashed; little Eve Parish, up from a recent illness, as pale as a jasmine bloom, yet with eyes like stars in her intense excitement; Andy Boles, on his crutches—Andy who had never walked quite right, and who seemed to be getting worse as the days went by; Mary Curry, her face shining from the harsh soap she had used, part of her black hair untangled by combing, part of it a wild snarl—these and many others: the children of the poor, came to the big house. They were very shy at first, very ill at ease before the great people in the beautiful home. Their blinking eyes took in the wide halls, the sparkling crystal chandeliers, the laden table spread the length of the great high-ceilinged dining room.

Colonel J. Morgan Lindsey and Miss Caroline greeted their guests cordially, while the black faces of Mose and Ivory and little Tobe peered through a crack of the kitchen door, curious to note how the "pore white trash" behaved themselves on such an occasion.

Never before had the children seen such a magnificent feast: the turkeys brown on their platters; the sweet potatoes fluffed and frosted with marshmallows; the grits, golden with giblet gravy; the cranberries like rubies in their crystal bowls; and finally, the roasted pecans, gathered from the Lindsey pecan groves; the frozen delicious cream—cream from the great jersey herds, and the cake that had been whipped to feathers by Ivory's black hands.

Then the tree, the peak of joy, flashed on their view as the great doors were flung open at last. Its brilliant beauty was enough to blind the strongest eyes: tinsel like rain in the sunlight; baubles that glittered with blue and crimson and gold lights from its frosted depths; a huge star teetering on its tip; countless firefly lights blinking through the branches at the dazzled and breathless children.

Colonel J. Morgan Lindsey himself distributed the gifts. It eased the hurt in his heart, someway, as he handed them out to these children of the poor—each child receiving all that his or her arms could hold. The big house had never before witnessed such unbounded joy. Mose and Ivory, peeping through the doors, were dumbfounded at the sight. At last Ivory found her tongue:

"Ah spects Ah never will git cleaned up aftah them pore white trash, but they sho does look shiney glad, an' Lor', Mose, the Big Boss-Man, an' Mis' Ca'oline, they looks glad, too. I spect they had needed baptism like as fiah before they could come up about little Mis' Ca'oline, and this look like it is it."

After the wild excitement and joy of receiving the gifts, Miss Caroline suggested that the lights be turned out, and with only the firelight on the grate, and the glow from the great tree, she sat down at the piano, and the music of the old sweet carols rang through the rooms, Miss Caroline leading, and the children's voices, silent at first, then at Miss Caroline's insistence timidly lifting, some of them sweet and clear, some tuneless, but making up for it with great volume:

> O little town of Bethlehem,
> How still we see thee lie,
> Above thy deep and dreamless sleep
> The silent stars go by
>
> Yet in thy dark streets shineth
> The everlasting Light. . . .

Miss Caroline watched the children through a mist of tears, her heart yearning for her own child with an unutterable longing. Then again the radiant golden vision bringing its assurance of happiness beyond any mortal dreaming. The golden light seemed to move, to fall like a halo about little Eve Parish, the pale child just up from a recent illness. The starry eyes caught and held Miss Caroline's until her fingers stumbled a bit over the keys. Little Eve, who needed mothering so; who needed food and clothing and medicine; who would be beautiful if she were loved and tended—who reminded her somewhat of little Caroline: the lovely blue of her eyes, her hair filled with honey colored lights—the look of heaven about her . . . .

They sang again:

> Silent night, holy night,
> All is calm, all is bright,
> Round yon virgin mother and child. . . .

Always the mother for the child—the child for the mother! Miss Caroline could go no farther in her singing. The sudden urge to mother all the children of the earth was clamoring in her heart. A universal motherhood! Why could she not spend the rest of her life in work among the lowly? The little Christ Child was lowly. Would she not be serving Him by serving these children clustered about her here? There was time and money—plenty of time, enough money. If she could know what to do—how to go about it. She would ask God, He would tell her. Perhaps she would be able to climb out of the dark valley of self-absorption and despair up to the golden hills of light through service. She might really be helpful to these children at her back door; might help them to higher and better living. If she only could! Then perhaps little Caroline's death would not be in vain—perhaps it was true that God does make all things work together for our good if we love Him enough. . . .

The lights were turned on again, and Colonel Lindsey suggested that they gather on the veranda to see the fireworks, so much a part of a southern Christmas that the party would not have been complete without such a demonstration. Morgan Lindsey, pompous and important at his assigned task, was master of ceremonies, and the children, warmly wrapped against any possible winter chill, and carefully guarded from harm, watched the beautiful, breath-taking rockets climb the sky and burst in a shower of glory. They cried out at the loveliness of the gold and crimson and blue balls of the Roman candles that broke against the night in sudden blazing splendor. They shivered with delight over the huge sparklers sending their white stars upward, outward, in bouquets of brightness, and they gave little shrieks of laughter at the firecrackers' violent explosions, and at the fizzers that could not quite find the power to take their fiery way through the night.

Miss Caroline stepped quietly over beside little Eve Parish, who stood apart from the others.

"Honey," she asked, "where do you live?"

"T'other side of Possum Run, in the hollow by the creek," the child answered shyly.

"Have you any brothers and sisters, dear?"

"No, ma'am. I live with my uncle and aunt and cousins. Lots of cousins. See, there's Jimmie an' Red an' Hettie an' Jeff an' Mattie," she pointed them out among the other children, "an' the baby's at home."

"I'm coming to see you soon," Miss Caroline said. "May I?"

"Oh yes, ma'am. I would like that." Her eyes were starrier than ever, but they grew suddenly troubled. Was not Miss Caroline the most beautiful person she had ever seen? Her eyes, her hands, her ways? But what would uncle Joe and aunt Het say? How would they behave? Perhaps they would be ugly and cross to Miss Caroline, the beautiful lady.

Tears sprang to the child's eyes. "I want yo' to come," she said, "but maybe yo' best not. Yo' see my uncle and aunt—they—they don't always treat company so good."

"I will come anyway," Miss Caroline smiled. "I will come just to see you. Shall we say I will tomorrow?"

"Well'um." The little girl gave a half glad, half frightened assent. And so it came about that the next afternoon the great limousine from the big house stopped at the tumble-down gate of the Joe Hart home, and Morgan Lindsey, very proper and proud in his new Christmas livery, opened the car door for Miss Caroline to alight. Little Eve, who had been eagerly awaiting her coming, stood back from the broken window pane, paler than usual with conflicting emotions.

"What she want here?" Aunt Het exclaimed, catching sight of the visitor from the window. "She never come befo'. What's she wantin' now?"

No one made reply, and Aunt Het herself opened the door. "What yo' want?" she asked, a barbed hostility in her voice. "We ain't got nothin' in common with such as yo'."

Old Joe Hart arose from his rickety chair. "She's right. We don't need ya. Ya ain't paid us no mind before last night. What's on ya mind?"

"Please," Miss Caroline pleaded, "may I come in, just for a minute? I want to talk to you about little Eve."

"What yo' want to say 'bout that pindlin' youngun? She's no good to yo' or us either, al'ays around sick an' whinin'."

"I came to ask if I might take her home with me. She is ill. She shows it. She needs food and care and medicine. I should be glad to take her and care for her as I would my own daughter, if you will allow me to do so."

A slyness had crept into Joe Hart's small beady eyes. "So ya want my niece, do ya? What ya want her for? Maybe now if ya make it worth my while I jest possibly might turn her over to ya, but not without. What ya offerin'?"

"I am not offering to buy little Eve as if she were your slave. I want to help her. I want to see her grow rosy-cheeked and well again." And Miss Caroline slipped to the child's side and put her arm lovingly about the shivering little figure.

"Well, ya ain't gittin' her . . . unless," Joe contemplated a moment, "unless maybe ya could git Colonel Lindsey to swap two or three of his mules fer her. They'd come in mighty handy for the gradin' work. How about a swap, Mis' Lindsey?" he leered.

"If you will sign a paper to that effect," Miss Caroline said sternly, "I think the exchange can be managed."

"Reckon so. We got too many kids anyhow. One less'll do no harm, I reckon."

Little Eve was suddenly transported with joy. The light of happiness was an aura about her, as she took her place beside Miss Caroline and rode home with her through the lovely southern winter twilight, to fill the vacancy in the big house, and in the hearts of the bereaved father and mother, and to become a beneficent influence in the lives of the darkies on the place. Then only did the stark horror fully lift from their superstitious hearts, for only the loyalty of the southern negro for their white folks had kept them on at the big house, so great was their fear of a "hant."

Miss Caroline realized the difficulties that lay ahead of her; the gigantic task she had undertaken. There would be the breaking down of the proud, stubborn wills of the parents of the neighborhood children, for there are no prouder people in the world than the born southerner. There would have to be improvements in the schools; education where there had been none before. There would be Andy, needing medical attention because of his lame hip; there would be all the other children with their various and endless needs; but surely if the Lord wanted a work done, He would direct that work, He would strengthen the laborer.

That night she knelt at her window facing the high, white, silent stars as she prayed for guidance, for wisdom, for strength for this strange universal motherhood that she had chosen to undertake, and surely little golden-hearted Caroline watched from the parapet of heaven, and was on tip-toe with gladness. Surely, He who had sent His only Son centuries ago to serve among the lowly, heard and answered her selfless prayer that starlit Christmas night.

Volume I - 1931

The First Christmas

Volume II - 1932

Volume III - 1933

Volume IV - 1934

Volume V - 1935

CHRISTMAS, 1940, the tenth annual volume edited by Randolph E. Haugan, is produced at Augsburg Publishing House, Minneapolis, Minnesota, by means of Photo-Mechanical Lithography. The body matter is set in linotype Garamond and the headings in monotype Goudy text with Lombardic capitals. This issue of CHRISTMAS appears in the year commemorating the five hundredth anniversary of Johannes Gutenberg's invention of printing from movable types.

Volume VI - 1936

Volume VII - 1937

Volume VIII - 1938

Volume IX - 1939